DEDICATION

Dedicated to the Absolute Divine
Truth That **YOU** Are!

Whole heartedly dedicated to
Lord Krishna, Lord Shiva,
Sri Ramana Maharshi and
Guru Nanak Dev Ji who have been and are
My Spiritual Guides on the path to
Self Realization and God Realization.

CONTENTS

ACKNOWLEDGMENTS

There are three friends that I have to absolutely acknowledge who knowingly or unknowingly led me to realize the Absolute Truth.

The first is Vik Sharma, the most hyperactive friend I have. He introduced me to Lord Krishna.

The second friend is Rajeev Aryan, an awakened being himself. He introduced me to the Bhagavad Gita and predicted that I would soon have a similar awakening.
This led to Self-Realization through complete surrender, love and devotion.

The third friend is Ranjan Sahu, a living encyclopedia of Spiritual Scriptures. He was sent by Lord Krishna to guide me on the path of knowledge, the Highest Truth.
This led to God-Realization through direct experiential knowledge.

"I Am Consciousness"

Part 1: See God With Open Eyes

Part 2: I Am Brahman

Part 3: Prepare To Awaken

Part 4: Kill The Ego!

Part 5: I'm Awake! Now What?

Part 6: I Am Conscious Ness

INTRODUCTION

This is the 5th Part of the series, "I Am Consciousness". It is highly recommend you read the earlier parts before commencing this one.

In the 1st part titled, "See God With Open Eyes" the main character of the series, David, a much sought after heart surgeon in New York City, arrives in New Delhi to embark on a spiritual journey of his life. He is received by his local guide Uchit and Yogiji from Swamiji's ashram in the Himalayan village known as Vatsalya Village. Three of them travel from New Delhi by train to Dehradun and from there by taxi to the ashram. In the almost eleven hour long journey, Yogiji explains to David what Brahman is and how to experience Brahman in every moment of his life.

In the 2nd Part titled, "I Am Brahman" David arrives at the ashram in Vatsalya Village and gets to meet Swamiji. Initially David throws some questions that were not clarified by Yogiji and Guruji. This is the final piece of the puzzle that Swamiji explains so lovingly and passionately. With great everyday examples, situations and logic, Swamiji explains that the reality of everyone is that same one Brahman. He explains and clears the doubts of all the new guests at the ashram including David, Uchit, Amelia, Oliver and Otto who also reached at the ashram on the same day as David.

In the 3rd Part titled, "Prepare To Awaken" Swamiji takes everyone step by step to understand exactly why the genuine seeker doesn't spiritually awaken even though he or she may have understood what all the Upanishads and Vedanta texts are saying. He describes in depth what is spiritual awakening and who or what is it that awakens. Different Spiritual paths are touched upon in conjunction with the path of knowledge.

In the 4th Part titled, "Kill The Ego!" David stays back at the ashram as everyone else leaves. He does everything to work his way to enlightenment for months until a visitor from Canada comes and plants a seed of doubt in David's mind about the whole enlightenment thing being a scam. Swamiji knew that David was a genuine seeker and was about to make the breakthrough very soon but Mark had given David's ego a chance of survival by doubting everything Swamiji had shared with him. Swamiji arranges for a one-on-one meeting in the old Satsang hall that hadn't been opened in over thirty years. An explosive conversation takes place through the night and David leaves the ashram to catch his flight back to New York. Swamiji knew David's ego would not survive the antidote that he had made sure David listened to intently. At the airport David has his breakthrough flash of enlightenment. He doesn't board the flight and is soon back at the ashram.

In this 5th Part, Swamiji shares with David all the different changes that take place after enlightenment. It's a huge paradigm shift of identity or the 'I' from the Ego to Brahman. Swamiji waits patiently as David goes through these changes before sending him back to New York to carry on with his life. David goes back home and within two years he retires from his work to settle in a farmhouse outside the city. He goes through all the stabilization stages after enlightenment and is finally compelled to share his wisdom of the Absolute Reality in his own words. Within a short span of time two shocking events take place that would change David's worldly life forever. You'll have to read on to find that out.

Happy reading....

I'm
Awake!
Now What?

I'M AWAKE! NOW WHAT?

THE HONEYMOON PERIOD

On the tenth day after David and Uchit were back at the ashram, Ramlal informed them that Swamiji would meet them in the garden area at midnight, *"Oh I almost forgot. Uchit, Swamiji asked you to bring along your notebook,"* said Ramlal.

David and Uchit walked onto the garden just a few minutes before midnight. Ramlal had set up two chairs facing Swamiji's main chair next to the pond. It was a chilly night and Ramlal had lit a fire on one side of the chairs.

David and Uchit took a stroll around the garden and looking up at the stars and moon he wondered how huge the Universe could be and if every star was a separate sun and had planets revolving around them, then it truly would be an infinite Universe.

Swamiji walked into the garden at precisely twelve midnight. They sat while Ramlal went into the kitchen. *"David, how have you been since you got back here?"* asked Swamiji. *"It's been good Swamiji, but there's a lot that I need to ask you and the first and main thing is I still can't find my mind. My ego and the feeling of 'I' or individualism has completely vanished. It has left a kind of blank space in my head. It's like my mind is there but its not like it was before. It's not doing anything, I'm not sure if I'm putting across what I want to say properly or not. It isn't easy to describe,"* said David.

"Sure David, I know what you're talking about and it's only now that you'll be able to understand what I have to say about spiritual enlightenment. Because from the unenlightened state it will sound stupid and foolish, almost like you have gone mad. If you told anyone I can't find my mind, they would advice you to see a psychiatrist immediately. It would be a grave matter of concern. Imagine the great heart surgeon of New York, David Smith, cannot find his mind. Everyone who looked forward to your magical treatment would flee from you. Yet in spirituality, it's the best thing that can happen to you. This is called the 'no-mind' state and I'll explain all this as we go along," said Swamiji.

"Uchit, get your marker out and write down the following topics that we will try to cover during our talks. And keep a tab on what we've discussed and remind me if we miss out anything," said Swamiji looking at Uchit with a smile.

8

Honeymoon Period,
Good, Evil & The Doer,
Desires, Thoughts, Gratitude,
Fear & Death,

Meditation & Third Eye,
All Spiritual Practices,
Screen of Consciousness,

Shifting Between Reflected
And Pure Consciusness,
Is More Knowledge Required?

Letting Go of Everything
Including Vedanta,
Adjusting To The Loneliness
of The Supreme Brahman,

Abiding In Pure Eternal Bliss,
Sahaja Samadhi or Turiya State,
How To Manage Work & Family
After Enlightenment,

Should You Become A
Spiritual Master?

"I'll start with the honeymoon period because that's what it seems like in the beginning," said Swamiji and continued, "The reason I didn't meet you for ten days is that I wanted the excitement of your initial state and experience to come down a little before we got talking. I'm sure the excitement level isn't as high as it was ten days earlier," "Yes Swamiji, at that time I was both excited and in disbelief that something like this is possible. I'm getting used to that now but my mind is still impossible to describe," replied David.

"You're experiencing a state of 'no-mind' or 'no-ego' right now," "Swamiji does that mean my mind and ego are gone completely?" blurted David. "No David, your mind and ego are still there but there's a shift in the way that they were working or being used earlier compared to now."

"Earlier your mind would think of everything as outside your body, your mind had a separation between the you the person and the rest of the Universe. The mind had things to do, needs to fulfill, goals to achieve and work your way up to what society projected as success. Your mind was attracted by numerous things around you and desires would make sure your mind was full of thoughts of all those things."

"All the pleasures and happiness of the entire Universe put together cannot give you the bliss you have experienced in those 5-7 minutes (enlightenment flash). Correct me if you think I'm wrong." "No Swamiji, you're absolutely right. The bliss that I experienced was indescribable. You're right that nothing in the world or Universe can even come close to that feeling. And I wouldn't exchange that for anything, ever," replied David.

"David, think of all the pleasures you've had in your life, add to that, all the happiness you can ever get out of attaining everything that you could ever want. Include holiday trips, name, fame and fortune, delicious food, expensive cars and homes, all the money you want, all the sex and dream relationships you'd like AND compare it to the 5-7 minutes of that enlightenment bliss," asked Swamiji.

"It can't be compared Swamiji. That bliss was complete and infinite. I can live the rest of my life based on that 5-7 minutes," replied David.

"Now your mind has nowhere to go. Your mind has experienced something that has shut it up. What possibly can you want or desire? What is there to think about? The mind is in as much a pleasant shock, as you are."

"There seems to be nothing left for the mind to do and so the desires are automatically phased out. Without desire, what does the mind need to think about? So there's an empty space kind of a feeling in the mind right now. This will soon fade away as the mind gradually settles into your Brahman-Self. The same can be applied to your ego or 'I' feeling. What can the ego want now having realized that the person is different and separate from you (Brahman-Self)?"

"The mind and ego don't disappear or vanish after enlightenment. They are very much still a part of the person and will continue to stay that way till the person dies. What has happened is a huge paradigm shift of identity from ego (mind-body complex/person) to Brahman (Infinite Existence and Consciousness). Your identity, your 'I' has found a new dimension which is not your mind or body. It's like the 'I' has been separated from the person and can witness everything that the person is doing and going through without being affected."

"The mind is designed to help the person survive in this world and it will continue to do that. The ego remains the 'I' of the person and will continue to be that. That's why the Saint or Sage can say both, 'I am Pure Consciousness' and 'I also have a body, I eat and sleep,' etc."

"This is because the Sage can communicate from three different dimensions or levels or states as you will. At the Absolute level, he is Pure Consciousness or Brahman. As the Universal level or God, he is a part of the Universe or a part of God. And at the Individual level, he or she is a separate person like everyone else."

"To communicate with the world you have you use your mind-ego identity. You can't walk around telling everyone you are Brahman or Pure Consciousness. To communicate with God you have to look upon Him/Her/It as the Whole and your person as a part. At the Absolute level there is no one to communicate with."

"So when you're at home you can be David the son, husband, father, brother or whatever role you're playing in the family, at work you can be David the surgeon and at your place of worship you can be David the devotee. But underlying all these states, you are firmly established in your Brahman-Self, the Absolute Reality in which David, God and the Universe appears."

"Back to the honeymoon period. You will feel like a huge burden called 'me' has been lifted off your back that you had been carrying for so long. It's a huge relief. You will feel like shouting and telling everyone what you have now realized because it's right in front of everyone but no one seems to see what you now see."

"My advice is to try and control yourself as much as you can especially around people who are not into non-duality or don't have a spiritual inclination. They will think you are nuts and have gone crazy, and no matter what you say, they won't believe you. There's a time and place and the right people to talk to about this and I'll discuss that with you later."

"During this initial time you may find very ordinary things as extraordinary. Simple things such as sunlight, rain, a flower, clouds, animals etc. will seem like you've never really appreciated what they are. They will seem like you've never paid attention to them before and they also may give you a certain kind of happiness by simply observing what now seems like divinity in them."

"At times you may feel so connected with what you're perceiving through the senses that it will leave you in tears of joy, like you're connected to God. A great song may bring tears to your eyes or you may feel connected to the air and everything else around you so strongly that you feel your own presence everywhere you turn. A mere mention of God by anyone will bring tears to your eyes."

"These are just some examples. You will experience different ones in different situations, but I just want to make you aware of it," said Swamiji. "Swamiji, why does it happen?" asked David. "Well, this happens because all the separate things that are perceived in and by your mind, start to feel connected as one, in the one pure consciousness that you are. This will happen in frequent small glimpses and then become quite normal for you and at a later stage you will actually be able to shift between reflected consciousness and pure consciousness at will."

"And lastly because the enlightenment flash experience is so blissful and indescribable, many people try to 'hold on' to the feeling or experience. You can't hold on to it but should simply surrender to it. There is nothing to hold on to, so any effort in that direction will disappoint you. Many others look forward to 'another' such flash. They try to recreate the entire scenario of when it happened. They try to understand why and how it happened so they can experience it again."

"To burst your bubble let me confirm that it won't happen again but what WILL happen is that you will gradually grow into that same bliss in a relatively short amount of time. During the enlightenment flash your mind was not there at all. The mind may only recall the few seconds as you went 'into' and 'came out' of the flash. During the bliss and dissolution, your mind wasn't active at all. So with time your mind will accept the shift fully and you will abide as pure bliss."

"There's more but let's take a short tea break and I'll continue from here. Uchit would you like to summarize what I have said so far in your notebook?" asked Swamiji, looking at Uchit with a smile, "Oh go on Uchit, don't let me down," said Swamiji playfully. Uchit opened a new page and wrote down...

No-Mind & No-Ego State Is Because Suddenly The Mind Experienced The Ultimate Bliss That Is Far Beyond Anything It Could Ever Desire Or Imagine!

It Has Nothing Left To Think About Or Desire Anymore!

The Ego Has Lost Identity Of You And Is Now The Identity Of Only Your Person (Body-Mind Complex)!

I'M AWAKE! NOW WHAT?

There's A Paradigm Shift From Reflected Consciousness To Pure Consciousness!

The Identity or 'I' Shifts From The Ego To Brahman-Self!

The Sage Uses 'I' In Three Ways:
I Am An Individual!
I Am A Part Of The Universe Or God!
I Am The Absolute Reality!

You Start To See The Divinity In Everything Around You Especially Nature.

A Mere Mention Of The Creator/God Will Bring Tears To Your Eyes.

These Are Glimpses Of Pure Consciousness, Your Brahman-Self!

Don't Try To 'Hold On' To The Bliss Feeling Or Recreate The Enlightenment Experience, You Can't!

I'M AWAKE! NOW WHAT?

DAWN OF ENLIGHTENMENT

After the short tea break and strolling around the garden under the moonlight and stars they all took a seat again and Swamiji carried on with his talk.

"David, *I'm revealing to you all the changes that I can think of because some may or may not become apparent to you. It's better to be aware of them so you can recognize them when they do take place. There's also one certain development which will occur after which I will have to let you go back to your country and carry on with your prescribed duties of a doctor, but I won't tell you which one it is as yet,*" said Swamiji ever so politely.

"*Soon you will feel as though your body and mind, or person, is really doing things as they come. Nothing is being 'done' by 'you'. Everything will simply feel like it happening on it's own. Your body and mind will do what is to be done but 'you' have no feeling of 'doer ship' anymore, as you had earlier. With this development you will stop judging anything or anyone anymore. The sense of doing good or bad will vanish. Of course you still know what is good and what is bad but 'you' will 'rise' above good and bad. Can you explain why this would happen David?*" asked Swamiji.

"*Let's see,*" said David scratching his head, "*All the activities are done by the person (body-mind) and I am not the person therefore in reality 'I' am not doing anything but witnessing what the person is doing. The sense of doer-ship is lost there itself, and if 'I' (Brahman-Self) am not doing anything then there is no question of me doing good or bad things. Is that logical Swamiji?*" replied David looking at Swamiji for some confirmation.

"*Absolutely right David,*" said Swamiji, "*You are Brahman and Brahman doesn't do anything but witnesses everything. Now that your mind also understands this, it will not have any reason to judge anything or anyone ever. Things are just they way they are due to the higher divine power of the Universe or God but you as Brahman have no-role to play in that. Great! Let's talk about another one,*" said Swamiji.

"If you have been praying to God, you will no longer feel the need to pray for anything material or spiritual. In fact the only thing you can do with God is be awestruck at His creation (even though you know it's just an appearance). You may at most offer gratitude and let your mind enjoy the experience called 'life' with all its ups and downs. Don't be surprised if you find yourself not praying for anything at all," said Swamiji.

"And what's the reason for that Swamiji?" asked David. "Well, there will be no desires left in your mind, nothing to achieve and there's nothing in the world that will give you any more happiness. In fact you'll realize that you already are everything, what could you possibly want? Selfish desires completely vanish. You don't want anything from God anymore."

"With all the worldly desires gone, almost ninety percent of your thoughts will vanish too. You'll realize that you have a mind that is under your control and you will use it only when you need to. You won't entertain any of it's tactics to keep you busy thinking about things that don't matter."

"Just as you have arms and legs and you use them when you need to, in the same you have a mind that you will use to 'think' when you need to. With fewer thoughts, you will abide as awareness most of the time and as you continue to abide as awareness, you'll find yourself enjoying the peace and bliss more and more without being judgmental about anything or anyone anymore. In fact 'thinking' will become a distraction and something that disrupts your peace and bliss."

fear

fear-less

"Let's talk about fear and the fear of death. Brahman is unborn and can never die. Once you've completely identified yourself as Brahman, there remains nothing in the Universe to fear. You actually become fearless of any situations, people and circumstances. Fear vanishes, including the fear of death that you had earlier. The unenlightened person fears old age and death because what is beyond death is the unknown."

death

"But the Sage experientially knows himself to be immortal and also knows that only the person dies, not him. So, gradually as you get used to abiding as awareness, you'll realize that once the body drops, you will remain intact as Brahman. The feeling would be like when a clay pot breaks and the space inside merges with the space outside without moving an inch, in fact the space was never divided, it just appeared that way because of the pot."

"*The body will drop and you will remain as Brahman exactly as you were while abiding as awareness. The Sage actually looks forward to death of the body because it means abiding as pure bliss eternally after that.*"

"*There's one spiritual practice I'll strongly urge you to carry on with and that is meditation.* The reason I'm saying this is because it will help activate and awaken your third eye that is at the point between your eyebrows. I know you are already meditating on that point, so keep doing that and let it develop. The third eye is not like your normal eyes; it is actually a 'sense' that will enable you to shift your focus between reflected consciousness and pure consciousness. We spoke about reflected consciousness and pure consciousness in our first talk (I Am Brahman) so I won't go over it again now. (Don't worry if you've forgotten, we'll cover it again as the story unfolds)

carry on meditation

3rd eye

"*With the third eye activated and the ability to shift between pure and reflected consciousness, you will soon be able to see (actually see with your eyes). the difference between the appearance of the world and its underlying reality. All the sages claim that the world is illusory, everything here is an appearance and not real. The Universe is projected by you on yourself and witnessed by you. These are not mere metaphors. Those who totally immerse themselves and abide as their Brahman-Self actually see all this* and I'll explain it logically to you later."

"*Let's talk about all the other spiritual practices that you have been doing. Should you carry on doing them or not? Well I'm not going to send you on another trip to Vivaan, Aarav and Chirag chachu to ask them but I'll try to answer your questions as they would. David I want you to pretend you are at Vivaan chachu's home and are asking him these same questions. I'll pretend to be Vivaan chachu and answer on his behalf.*"

"Sure Swamiji," replied David and continued, "*Vivaan chachu, I recently had a flash of enlightenment wherein I dissolved into the vast emptiness or nothingness of Brahman. I did follow your advice of doing selfless work for many months before this happened. I'd like to know if I should carry on doing the same selfless work and if so, for how long?*" asked David looking at Swamiji.

"*It's so great to see you again David,*" replied Swamiji imitating Vivaan chachu's body language and accent. David and Uchit were both surprised at how well Swamiji imitated Vivaan.

"*Well David, if you have realized your Brahman-Self, then the selfless work practice has done its job. Now tell me David, as your Brahman-Self what can you want for yourself? How can you become selfish now?*"

"*Brahman doesn't need anything and doesn't do anything. However, your mind and body will continue to do things out of natural compassion for others. You have transcended pain and suffering but will find it difficult to see others in pain. You have no choice; selfless work will continue to happen through your person on its own. Once you are fully established as Brahman even if you don't do anything, just your presence around people will benefit them. Don't worry about 'doing' selfless work, it will happen naturally through this body-mind complex, you cannot become selfish again in any way. From Brahman's point of view everything is temporary, is unreal, is illusory, is limited and you are the underlying reality of everything. The Ocean cannot want or desire small waves,*" replied Swamiji.

"*Okay, that's good to know Vivaan chachu, I don't have anything more to ask. I guess I just have to 'be' and selfless work will continue to be done through this mind-body complex,*" said David.

"*Great!*" Exclaimed Swamiji, "*Let's go to Aarav chachu's place and ask about the path of love and devotion,*" said Swamiji.

"*Aarav chachu, after the flash of enlightenment should I continue to love, worship and pray to God and if so, then for how long?*" asked David.

"*David,*" replied Swamiji in Aarav's chachu's voice, "*I was in love with God before enlightenment and just because I'm enlightened now, I can't give up my love for God. The intention of my love was never to become enlightened. Enlightenment came through the Grace of God. I cannot stop loving and worshipping God just because I'm enlightened now, that would be so selfish. I personally will continue to love and worship God till the day this body drops dead. That is my personal choice. You will have to go by your instincts and what you personally feel about God. If you truly loved God, it would be hard and wrong to forsake that love. Having said that, its totally okay if you don't love or worship Him/Her/It after enlightenment because you have realized the underlying truth of God and your true nature to be one and the same Brahman. It is absolutely your call but I'll tell you, the joy of loving God in duality after realization of non-duality is simply beautiful and divine,*" replied Swamiji acting as Aarav chachu.

"*That's great Aarav chachu, I don't really have anything more to ask,*" said David. "*Let's quickly do Chirag chachu and the path of meditation,*" said Swamiji excitedly like he was enjoying imitating their characters.

"*Chirag chachu, should I continue with my meditation after enlightenment and if yes, for how long?*" asked David looking at Swamiji.

"My dear David, meditation helps keep your mind calm and clear. I practice meditation daily and in fact I teach others how to meditate so, I have been doing it even after my enlightenment. But even after I retire I'm sure I will always start my day with an hour of meditation in the morning. This is just my personal choice because the practice has become a routine and if I don't start my day with that hour of meditation, I don't feel good. It's like when you start exercising and begin to enjoy it everyday, then missing even a day makes you feel bad about it. I don't do it to achieve anything more but I do it for the love of meditation and starting my day with a clean and calm mind. Like I said, it's my personal choice, you can continue if you want to or not, it's entirely up to you. If you do continue, it will help you establish yourself fully as Brahman quicker than if you didn't. It's your call. Suppose you were offered a role as the main lead in a Hollywood movie and you trained in the gym and ate healthy foods for months to get your body in shape for the role. After the film shooting gets over, it's entirely up to you if you want to become fat again or keep up the fitness routine that made you healthy and fit," said Swamiji.

"So Swamiji, what I've understood is that it would be entirely up to me if I would like to carry on with the spiritual practices or not. They're not really required but its advisable to carry on doing them until I actually intuitively feel its time to let go of them," said David looking at Swamiji.

"That's a good summary and very well understood my boy!" Exclaimed Swamiji clapping his hands.

"Swamiji," interrupted Uchit, *"I have a question as well. Can I ask it please?"* asked Uchit, who was listening intently to everything that was being discussed. *"Sure Uchit, please ask,"* replied Swamiji thinking it would be one of those silly questions that Uchit usually asked. *"Swamiji, since the first day that I came to the ashram with David sir, I've never seen you do any spiritual practice at all. We've never seen you meditate or worship any God. We haven't seen you reading any scriptures or books on spiritual knowledge. However, regarding selfless work I agree that you are doing a tremendous service at the ashram by sharing your wisdom with others. How come you don't do any other spiritual practices including reading up more knowledge Swamiji?"* asked Uchit much to the amazement of both David and Swamiji.

"That's a good observation Uchit," replied Swamiji, *"I'll tell you about that later as well. Let's stop here for today. I think you have enough food for thought. David, in the next few days we may bump into each other but regarding our next talk, I'll let you know when we'll have it. It won't be too soon,"* said Swamiji, *"Uchit, before we leave would you be kind enough to show us the notes you took down?"* asked Swamiji. Uchit opened the pages where he had scribbled with his marker and read out aloud...

I'M AWAKE! NOW WHAT?

Brahman Does Nothing
So The Sense Of
Doer-ship Is Lost!

You Rise Above
Good & Evil!

You Stop Judging
Anyone Or Anything!

Prayers For Material
Things Will Stop!

You Become Fearless
Of Everything
Including Death!

You Know You Will
Abide As Brahman
After Death Of The
Body!

The Third-Eye Is A
'Sense' That Allows
You To Shift Between
Reflected And Pure
Consciousness At Will!

No Spiritual Practices
Are Required Or
Essential Anymore But
You May Carry On
With Them If You Like!

I'M AWAKE! NOW WHAT?

VATSALYA MARKET PLACE

David continued to help around the ashram with the daily chores. He also carried on his routine of starting the day with an hour of meditation and talking to God on the nearby hilltop. Meanwhile Uchit served clients around the village and nearby areas who required taxi services. Ramlal also called for Uchit's taxi service whenever they needed transportation for visitors at the ashram.

A couple of months went by and David recognized the changes taking place within him just as Swamiji had described. On a few occasions when he opened his eyes after meditation on the hilltop, everything in the valley felt connected to him. The birds, little animals and trees with exotic flowers, the sunlight and the mountains in the horizon all seemed part of one huge dance of consciousness. It was a divine feeling and often filled his eyes with tears.

He spoke to God like he was addressing himself. His mind was under control with no haywire thoughts rushing in and disturbing the calmness that his mind was getting used to. Just remaining as the observer of everything that was going on, he had stopped judging anything or anyone. Everything was happening as it should and it was all okay just the way it was. Nothing was good or bad, everything felt divine. He had also stopped fearing anything at all, including death. It became certain that death of the body could take away nothing from his immortal Self.

One fine morning as Uchit, David and Ramlal were having breakfast, Swamiji walked into the garden area and joined them. "*All going well David?*" asked Swamiji as Ramlal served him the hot '*aloo paranthas*' (chapattis with mashed potato filling and spices), curd and mango pickle, a popular north Indian dish that Swamiji enjoyed.

"*Yes, I think so Swamiji. I am experiencing most of the changes you told me about. In fact I want to thank you for the talk we had two months back. If it weren't for your guidance I would have wasted a lot time and effort in trying to figure out what was going on. Your words came to mind every time something new happened and my mind was able to easily accept the changes without resistance,*" replied David.

"Really? What all have you experienced so far my boy?" asked Swamiji and David narrated everything that was going on. "Are you still on a mission Mister David Smith?" asked Swamiji raising his eyebrows, (All these changes usually take place between six months to a year) and it's only been a couple of months since you came back and we had our first talk. Have you been anywhere outside the ashram lately?" asked Swamiji looking at David directly into his eyes like he was scanning his mind.

"No Swamiji, I've just been at the ashram except for my morning meditation that I go for, on the nearby hilltop," replied David. "Uchit, are you free today?" asked Swamiji still looking at David. "Yes Swamiji, free and at your service," replied Uchit with a huge smile. "We had ordered some books for the library and the local bookstore has received them today. Can you please go and collect them? There is only one bookstore in the market that is towards the end of the main street just before Panshul's Fair. David please go with Uchit, there should be about three hundred books," requested Swamiji still looking at David.

"Sure Swamiji, we'll leave immediately," said David and they finished their breakfast and left for the market in Uchit's car. Swamiji remained seated at the table for quite some time even after finishing his breakfast. "Swamiji, is everything okay? I'm just asking why you sent them to collect the books when the bookstore had promised to deliver them to the ashram on the weekend?"

"*Oh yes Ramlal,*" replied Swamiji like he came out of a trance. "*I just thought it would be a good break for David. He's been only around a few people at the ashram for too long. A visit to the market will refresh his mind and he may buy some items that he needs,*" replied Swamiji. Ramlal wasn't convinced; he knew Swamiji too well but preferred not to probe him any further. He quickly cleared the table and went into the kitchen.

Uchit found a parking spot near the *Witness Circle.* David looked up to see the stationary partridge and then looked on the lower branches of the tree to see the other partridges that were very busy doing all sorts of activities. As they crossed the road onto the main street David rubbed his eyes and blinked them a few times. He couldn't comprehend what he was seeing. There was so much activity going on on the street compared to the calm ambience of the ashram. However, this was not new to him but what he was seeing was something new. People were rushing on the footpaths, vendors were selling all sorts of snacks and drinks on the roadside, there were stray dogs running around and shopkeepers standing outside the shops luring tourists.

Everything that David was seeing appeared to be on a huge giant flat screen. It looked like a live video being projected on the biggest screen you can imagine. It was exactly like seeing a movie being projected on a flat screen with the exception that this was happening in real life on the street and everywhere he turned around to look. He also felt like he knew what was behind the screen but the eyes and mind couldn't comprehend anything.

David stopped on the side for a few seconds and splashed his eyes with some cold water. But again, as he looked around the busy market, it was like a movie playing in front of him. Nothing seemed real. As they kept walking up the street David remembered that Aabha from the marble artifact shop was an enlightened being.

They walked in and finding no one in the shop, they went through the backdoor into the backyard where Aabha was working on one of his masterpiece statues. They greeted each other and David asked him if he knew anything about what he was experiencing.

screen of Consciousness

"*Oh that?*" replied Aabha, still working on his statue, "*That's the screen of consciousness,*" said Aabha. "*Screen of WHAT????*" Exclaimed David. "*Screen of consciousness. Very few enlightened people reach this milestone to actually be able to see it literally with their eyes. Come closer and let me show you. Take a good look at this masterpiece that I'm working on. Can you see it in 3D?*" asked Aabha. "*Of course I can. I have two eyes so I can see everything in 3D,*" replied David. "*Okay, now go outside the shop and look at the street again,*" said Aabha.

David went out to the street and was back in a flash, "*You're right! I can see this statue in 3D but the busy street is in 2D, and I'm not doing anything deliberately. Why is it happening?*" asked David in disbelief. "*I'm sorry but I don't have the time to explain all this today. This statue must be delivered by tomorrow morning and I still have a lot to do. If you're in the market for some time, go and meet Panshul in his office. The fair will be closed but he should be in his office today,*" replied Aabha and bid them goodbye.

"*We're headed there anyway. Uchit, you go to the bookstore and have the boxes ready meanwhile I'll go and have a word with Panshul. I'll meet you at the bookstore as soon as I'm done,*" said David as he rushed towards Panshul's Fair.

Panshul was in his office and recognized David. *"It' so good to see you after so long. How's Swamiji doing?"* asked Panshul. *"He's doing great,"* replied David and asked him about the screen of consciousness. *"Yes my dear, that's a metaphor used to explain that our true Self is like the screen on which the Universe is projected. The screen isn't separate from the images projected on it and at the same time it is completely unaffected and undisturbed by what is projected on it,"* replied Panshul

"I already know all this but I can literally see it in real life. The busy street appears to be projected like a live video on a huge flat screen and I am watching the images on the screen, and I am also everything behind the screen. How or why is this happening?" asked David unable to control his excitement.

"Oh, I've never experienced it myself but I know that very few enlightened people with their third eye activated and heightened awareness can experience it in reality. You have to be able to shift between reflected consciousness and pure consciousness in your mind to be able to see this. I'm sorry I have no idea of why and how it happens," replied Panshul and David left in hurry to join Uchit and the bookstore. They carried the boxes to the car and left for the ashram.

"*I remember noting down (the screen of consciousness as one of the topics to be covered by Swamiji but he didn't say anything about it,)* said Uchit as he drove. "Hmmmm, *(screen of consciousness, shifting between reflected and pure consciousness, third eye activation?) I can't wait for Swamiji to explain all this,*" thought David to himself as they drove into the ashram parking lot.

Ramlal was quick to come out and help Uchit carry the boxes into the reception area. "*Place the boxes here. The books have to be stamped with the ashram rubber stamp and dated before they're put in the library,*" explained Ramlal. "*Sure, we'll help you,*" replied David as Ramlal handed them a couple of dated rubber stamps and an inkpad from behind the counter.

"*Something weird happened today,*" said David to Ramlal. "*I KNEW IT!!!* Exclaimed Ramlal. "*What do you know?*" asked David curiously. "*We had paid extra delivery charges to the bookstore to have the books delivered to the ashram and they were going to do that on the weekend but when Swamiji asked you to go and pick them up, I knew there was something fishy. Anyway, tell me what happened,*" replied Ramlal, and David narrated everything to him.

"Screen of consciousness? WOW!!! I know all about it. I've heard Swamiji speak about it only once but it was so fascinating that I remember it all. I've also read about it in some books. It is supposed to be unbelievable when you see if for the first time. I'm not telling you anything more about it, it wouldn't be right," said Ramlal. "I guess I'll just have to wait for Swamiji to call for our next talk," sighed David. "And that would be tonight at 9pm," blurted Ramlal, "Yes, after you left, Swamiji was still at the table for quite sometime immersed in deep thought. When he woke up to leave he told me to inform you of tonight's meeting at 9pm," said Ramlal.

"Not midnight?" asked Uchit, "No. Swamiji usually starts his talks at midnight but whenever he feels that he needs more time, then he starts at 9pm and takes two breaks, one at midnight and another at 3am. Remember your meeting at the Satsang hall started at 9pm too?" reminded Ramlal and David's whole body shook and trembled for a few seconds.

"Please don't talk about that hall again. I still get chills up my spine whenever I think of it. I don't think I would ever step into that hall again, and besides, that night I walked out of the meeting at 3am because I couldn't take any more of what was going on," said David shaking his head.

I'M AWAKE! NOW WHAT?

SCREEN OF CONSCIOUSNESS
(9pm To 12 Midnight)

All was set as usual in the lawn. With the lights and starry sky, the same lawn looked so different in the night compared to the daytime. Uchit had his notebook and marker ready because it seemed like this would be a long night and David wanted all the major points to be noted down for future reference.

"Did you buy anything from the market for yourself," asked Swamiji as he walked onto the grass and took his seat. He had a huge grin on his face. *"No Swamiji, we collected the books and came back. I met Aabha and Panshul before we returned. We also helped Ramlal stamp and date the books when we got back,"* said David very calmly like nothing had happened.

"Thank you David. And I do appreciate all your help at the ashram. We'd better start, there's a lot to cover tonight. Uchit, please check where we stopped last time," said Swamiji. Uchit quickly opened the page where he had listed the topics and screamed, *"Screen of CONSCIOUSNESS!!!!"* with his hand in the air. *"What's the matter Uchit? Why are you so excited?"* asked Swamiji. *"No.... Umm... Nothing Swamiji,"* replied Uchit getting a grip on himself.

"Very well then. I think I'll skip this topic for now because it's a little advanced. What's the next topic Uchit?*"* asked Swamiji and David couldn't control his excitement anymore, *"Swamiji, I SAW the screen of consciousness today!"* *"Really? Is that so? And you cannot see it now?"* asked Swamiji looking at David with a smile.

"Not really Swamiji, it was very evident in the busy marketplace with everything going on. I can't really see it now. But Aabha and Panshul confirmed that I was seeing the screen of consciousness. Unfortunately none of them could explain anything more about it. Can you see the screen of consciousness Swamiji?" asked David wondering if Swamiji himself was that advanced.

"Of course David, that's the only way I see. I see Brahman everywhere. However, whenever I need to, I can choose to shift my perception to how the unenlightened person sees," replied Swamiji. "Whenever you choose to? You mean you can choose to change your perception of how you see?" asked David "That's right David. All right, let's talk about that first if you did see it. Once you understand how and why it happens logically (for the awakened person), then you will be begin to recognize it and learn how to make the shift mentally yourself," said Swamiji.

"Let me give you an example before the explanation. Imagine you walk into a cinema hall with someone who has never been to one before, and you explain to him beforehand that in the cinema hall pictures are projected in the form of light on a screen, by a projector that's at the opposite end of the hall."

"Unfortunately, when you walk into the hall, the movie has already begun and you take your seats. The entire screen is covered by light from the projector and your friend sees the movie just like he would see something in real life, only bigger."

"If he asked, and you tried to point out the screen while the movie is playing, it would be impossible for him to understand where and what the screen is. Anywhere you point on the screen there would some image projected on it that keeps changing. However, during the interval (Yes Bollywood movies have a short interval in between the movie), when the cinema lights come on and the movie is stopped for a few minutes, you can point out and show your friend what a screen is and where it is."

"He would have no difficulty understanding it now. It's a blank screen, which he can see and after the interval, he now knows that all the images are being projected as colored light on a flat screen. He can easily shift his focus and attention from the images to the screen and back at will. It's important to know where and what the blank screen looks like so that you know the reality of the movie when it's playing."

"Unfortunately for us as well, the movie of our life has already begun when we are born. There's no chance of seeing the blank screen when we came into the world and there's no interval in life for us to see it clearly then. We can however, experience the blank screen through meditation."

"David, I'm glad you continued with your meditation practice and this is a result of that practice. I'm explaining this to you because:

1. *You are enlightened and spiritually awake,*
2. *You have practiced meditation and,*
3. *You have NO DOUBT that you ARE the Infinite Awareness that you abide as, during meditation.*

"David, I'm sure that whenever you close your eyes, sit for meditation and focus on the third eye position, you immediately identify yourself as the infinite pure consciousness or awareness that you experience from that point," said Swamiji.

(Note: This will be difficult for anyone who doesn't meet these three conditions. If you ARE spiritually awake and still can't see the screen of consciousness it's because you may not have practiced meditation ON the Self AS the Self to the point where you can easily shift your consciousness between pure consciousness during meditation, and your reflected consciousness in your normal waking state.)

Pure Vs. Reflected Consciousness
Part 2 of "I Am Brahman"

Swamiji carried on, *"Let me briefly repeat what is meant by Pure Consciousness or Pure Awareness compared to Reflected Consciousness. We did cover this in depth on our first meeting under the full moon (Part 2: "I Am Brahman")."*

"Please note that I'm referring to the same Brahman-Self when I say Pure Awareness, Pure Consciousness, Self with a capital 'S' or Brahman. All theses terms mean the same thing."

"Your true identity is Pure Consciousness but your mind is also conscious. Your mind is conscious but not consciousNESS. It is aware but not awareNESS."

"The reason the mind is conscious or aware is that it 'reflects' pure consciousness and so the mind 'appears' to be conscious. And this conscious mind perceives everything from the external world through the five senses."

"The images captured in our eyes are recreated in the conscious mind and because we all have two eyes, we see everything in 3D. During meditation, your mind is alert, awake and aware (of the nothingness) while 'you' abide as pure awareness."

"What is perceived by the conscious mind would appear differently if we could shift the perception from reflected consciousness to pure consciousness. This is what has begun happening with you in small glimpses and you'll soon be able to shift your consciousness easily between the person and your true Self i.e. between Reflected Consciousness (Person/Mind) and Pure Consciousness (Brahman)."

54

Swamiji continued, *"Sitting in meditation with your eyes closed and meditating on the third eye (the point between the eyebrows) and abiding as pure consciousness or awareness increases the intensity of your awareness. The awareness expands into infinity around you. You ARE the Awareness and you are INFINITE (At this point it's not intellectual, it's a reality. If you still don't feel you are the Awareness, you need to spend more time in meditation)."*

"That should be the firm knowledge and reality. You can't see anything apart from a black blankness because your eyes are closed. When your awareness is highly developed due to meditation, you know very well that as soon as you shift your focus to the third eye position, you can abide as pure consciousness or pure awareness in an instant. Uchit hand me the notebook and let me make some drawings to illustrate it for better understanding," said Swamiji taking the notebook and making some drawings.

Step 1: Established As Brahman

"Here is a man meditating ON BRAHMAN AS BRAHMAN (Infinite Pure Existence & Infinite Pure Consciousness). His eyes are closed, and his energy is focused and concentrated at the third eye. From this point (third eye) he is abiding as Brahman or Pure Consciousness. Because his eyelids are closed, all he can see behind them is a dark and a black blankness. This is the 'blank screen' of your life," said Swamiji.

Pure Consciousness

+

Closed Eyes

=

Black & Blank 360° Movie Screen!

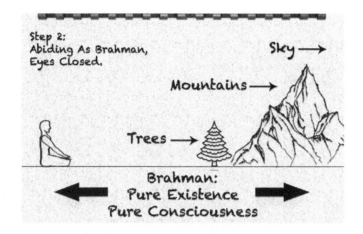

Step 2: Side View Of The Same

"This is a side view of the same man. There are three objects (for example purposes only) directly in front of him at different distances and of different heights. With a side view we will be able to analyze what happens when he opens his eyes."

"What we see through our eyes is only light that is reflected off the surfaces of objects. Keep in mind that light travels in a straight line, as you may already know."

Underlying Reality Of All Objects Is Pure Existence!
The Man Is Firmly Established As Brahman! The Trees, Mountains And Sky Are Nothing But Him.
(Pure Existence & Pure Consciousness)

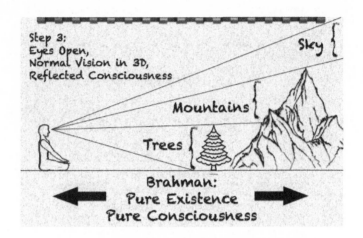

Step 3: Normal Sight

"The man opens his eyes and light reflected off the objects enters his eyes and an image of the objects is recreated in the mind. The mind is not a conscious entity but 'reflects' pure consciousness. This reflected consciousness is used by the mind to perceive all objects."

"The man has two eyes and so a 3D image is perceived by the mind that will give him an idea of the length, width and DEPTH of each object."

When The Eyes Open, The Mind Perceives The Objects Before Them Using Reflected Consciousness In 3D!

This Is How The Normal, Unenlightened Person Sees.

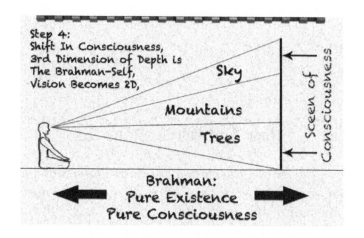

Step 4: Shift From Reflected Consciousness To Pure Consciousness

"With his eyes open, if the man shifts his consciousness from Reflected Consciousness to Pure Consciousness using the third eye, immediately the image will be perceived in 2D because there is only one third eye 'sense' and not two (Third eye sense eliminates space and thus the 3rd dimension of depth is eliminated)."

"The third eye perceives from Brahman's perspective; infinite, formless and non-dual all around in 360°. Immediately the depth disappears and the man sees in 2D (A screen is always in 2D, it has height and width, and is flat.)

Shifting From Reflected Consciousness To Pure Consciousness Changes A 3D Perception To 2D!
(2 Normal Eyes To 1 Third Eye)

How And Why It Happens

"While established as his Brahman-Self and his eyes open, light reflected off existing objects goes into the eyes. Light only reflects off the surface and doesn't penetrate the objects. This thin layer of light can be compared to the light reflected off the screen in a cinema hall. Everything in front of and behind this layer of light is Brahman-Self."

"There is no 'space' anymore in the visual perceived. Everything behind the layer of light is perceived as the Self (Pure Consciousness). So, the Sage sees (with his eyes) the landscape as a thin layer of light projected on his own Brahman-Self."

Only Light Enters The Eyes. Everything In Front And Behind The Light Is The Brahman-Self!

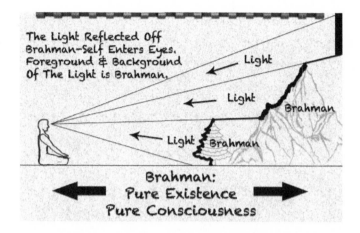

The thin layer of light reflecting off the surfaces of the trees, mountains and sky (**Darkened** lines above) enters the eyes. Behind this layer of light is Brahman-Self (Pure Consciousness & Existence).

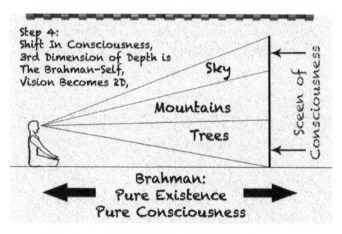

The thin film of light appears flat and in 2D just like a cinema screen. It's known as the "Screen of Consciousness."

This is what the Enlightened Person sees. The trees, mountains and sky (tree, mountain and sky are examples) all appear on a flat 2D screen of Consciousness. This applies to everything seen by the enlightened person when he or she shifts to Pure Consciousness.

With eyes closed (as in Step 1) the Sage abides as the 'blank' screen of Brahman. When he opens his eyes he sees the movie of life projected on the screen of Brahman (as in Step 4). Confusing? Not so for the enlightened Sage. He knows that it's only Brahman experiencing Brahman through the illusion of experience!

"How is it possible? Remember the underlying reality of everything is Brahman. All the objects 'exist' within your Brahman-Self. So from Brahman's point of view, everything seen by the eyes is just light falling on itself (the objects) and reflected into the eyes. Just as light in the cinema hall falls upon a screen and is reflected into the eyes, in the same way, light falls on the EXISTENCE of objects and is reflected into the eyes."

"Their existence is Brahman and the Pure Consciousness perceiving them is also Brahman.

Thus You As Brahman (Pure Consciousness) Perceive Your Own Pure Existence Through The Eyes And Mind.

Pure Consciousness Perceives Pure Existence!

Brahman Perceives Brahman! Thus All Perception Is Negated And Illusory! Only Brahman Exists! Brahman Is Non-dual!

David, only the Sage can understand this, and you are at the initial transition stage, learning to shift between Reflected and Pure Consciousness (Mind & Brahman). To the unenlightened person it will sound really crazy and unbelievable."

"In the mid 1990's a new craze or fad had arisen around the world called 'Stereograms'. These were 3D images perceived on a 2D flat sheet of paper. The images look like random patterns but if you shift your eyes towards each other slightly and stare at the pattern for sometime, the pattern starts to move gradually and magically transforms into a 3D image."

"To the person who couldn't do it, it seemed unbelievable and crazy, but to the one who could see it, it was like magic. Here's an example of a Stereogram. See if you can see the huge shark in 3D in the image on the next page."

"Bring the stereogram image really close to your eyes (until you touch it with your nose). At this distance your eyes cannot focus on the image and they look somewhere behind the image. Now, slowly push the image away from you, while trying to keep the eyes off focus. At some point you will see the hidden 3D image."

"This takes making a shift in the eyes. The same is applicable to a shift in Consciousness from Reflected Consciousness to Pure Consciousness. You can actually see how the world is an illusion or appearance on your true Brahman-Self."

This Side Up - Stereogram

I'M AWAKE! NOW WHAT?

3D Shark In The Stereogram

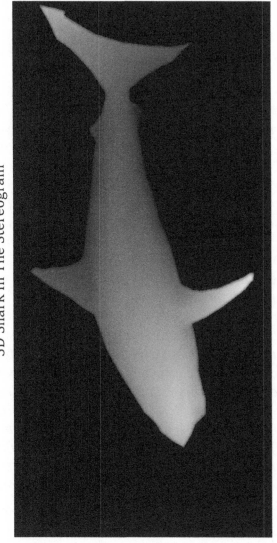

"David, this ability to shift Consciousness in an instant will answer many more questions as to how the enlightened person lives in the world," said Swamiji. *"All the promises made about the benefits of Self-Realization culminate to this ability to shift from the normal self to your true Self."*

"Transcending pain and suffering, realizing your immortality and conquering death, becoming fearless, all desires fulfilled, realizing the Universe is actually projected by your true Self upon itself and You remain as the untouched 'witness' of everything going on in the Universe and why the Universe is just an illusion and not real at all. All these statements will be realized now when you can shift from your person to your Brahman-Self in an instant."

"Let's use another cinema example now. Before enlightenment, we identify ourselves as a character in the movie (life), and after enlightenment we realize our true Self to be safely sitting as the audience (witness). The Enlightened Sage is still the character in the movie (he's still alive) but also knows that he is really the audience and not the character. The character will continue to go through the ups and downs in the movie (life) but as the audience he's absolutely untouched. We'll use this example to explain some more points but for now let's take a tea break," said Swamiji and they all got up. Ramlal had already laid the table.

FULL ENLIGHTENMENT
(Midnight To 3am)

After the break, Swamiji carried on from where he had stopped, *"David, the shift between reflected consciousness and pure consciousness or the ability to shift between the person and Brahman-Self is what I had been waiting for you to start recognizing. This is the milestone after which I have to let you go back home and carry on with your life and your worldly duties,"* said Swamiji looking at a stunned David.

"In the next few months, you will mostly abide as your Brahman-Self and act from the person's point of view only when required. You'll find the Brahman-Self completely peaceful and will try to avoid anything that disturbs that peace. So what I'm going to talk about now .are the changes that will naturally occur in the coming months when you're back home," said Swamiji.

"Uchit you asked me during our last talk why I don't meditate, worship, study or do any other spiritual practices. I'll be glad to answer this now, as it will cover a good amount of what I want to talk about anyway," said Swamiji.

"David, in a few months or at most a couple of years, full realization will completely dawn upon you. Vivaan, Aarav and Chirag chachu advised you to carry on with love, worship, meditation, selfless work etc. Yet you claim that you have not seen me doing any of these."

"Regarding selfless work, everything I do is automatically done for others; this ashram is a place for any genuine spiritual seeker to come and receive the wisdom that can free him or her from the bondages of life and death, pain and suffering. This is all that I do; I only share my wisdom with others to the best of my ability. We have no fees for the same, but regardless of that, I am compelled to share this wisdom. I cannot keep it to myself even if I tried to. I live a very simple life and have very few belongings; only the basic necessities are what I have. My life is a dedication to serving God through this person (body-mind). There is no reason to do anything for this body-mind complex."

"The Universe is perceived 'by' and 'in' my mind. The Universe is the projection of God. He is everywhere, every time and in everything. I love and respect every place, every time and everything, which includes every-body. I love God in everything I do. I need not go to a place of worship or practice any rituals to do that.

Wherever this body is, God is always present in everything all around it. I can't get rid of God even if I wanted to. So the question of 'going' to some place to worship God doesn't arise. God IS the Universe or the Universe IS God!"

"Let's take a look at meditation. I had mentioned sometime earlier that in true meditation there's no meditator. The purpose of meditation is to END meditation IN meditation THROUGH meditation. From the moment I wake up, I am immersed in my Brahman-Self, which means that I see, eat, breathe, talk, walk and everything else while immersed in the Self. I am 'in' meditation all the time, in every place and in everything that I do. I can't get out of meditation even if I wanted to. Therefore the need to meditate doesn't arise. I cannot do anything to meditate because I'm always in it."

"What about more spiritual knowledge? Brahman is knowledge itself. There is nothing that is apart from Brahman to know. Once you realize your Brahman-Self directly, you'll easily filter out what is the truth or not. All the scriptures talk of the same truth in different ways but after realization of the Self, your direct experience is your best teacher."

"So if you made a false statement and claimed that it was written in a Holy Scripture, I would immediately know whether it's talking about the truth or not regardless of where or who said it. After God-realization, what is true and what is false is very clear, nothing can shake or confuse you ever. There's no higher truth above Brahman for you to learn about or realize. The Enlightened Sage is firmly established in the Absolute Truth."

"There are a million paths that lead to the Absolute but when you're at the top of the mountain, you can see all the other paths that lead up to the same peak. It doesn't affect you in any way. Your direct life experience as your Brahman-Self will be your best guidance and teacher."

"Your 2+2 is now equal to 4 intellectually AND experientially. Your 'I' is now Brahman intellectually AND experientially. From here you can discover as many ways or paths to find out what leads to realizing Brahman or adding up to 4. The ways and paths are endless," said Swamiji.

*"You will slowly settle into the same state David, it's the most natural and effortless state of personhood. **You do without doing and don't do while doing.** I'll elaborate on this in sometime. Once you are fully stabilized in and as the Self, you will and should, automatically let go of everything, and I do mean everything. You should not hold on to any practice whatsoever. You even need to let go of all the knowledge you have learnt. The direct experience of being immersed in and as the Self will be complete in every way,"* said Swamiji.

"As you stabilize into your Brahman-Self and especially after you shift between reflected and pure Consciousness, you will see in reality that the world and Universe are just an 'appearance' within your Brahman-Self. For the Sage, the Universe is an illusion and he knows it for a fact through direct experience."

"As the audience, you know the movie is just an illusion and not really happening. David, you have started to get glimpses of the reality of the Universe and soon you will be able to see the reality behind every appearance of the Universe," said Swamiji. *"So, is everything ultimately an illusion Swamiji?"* asked David.

"From the point of the Absolute and the Enlightened Sage, yes, everything is an illusion. You will soon experience it directly yourself. The world to the enlightened person is as unreal as it is real to the unenlightened person," replied Swamiji.

"During this stabilization period you will realize most of the things that you did are not required, not essential and are in fact now posing as a distraction to your true nature. You will not feel the need to keep praying to God, no need to continue any mantra chanting you practiced, no more meditation is required, no more putting in an effort to do selfless work. At this point you may start to feel that everything you did is naturally being taken away from you. I want you to be aware that it's not only okay to let go but that you SHOULD let it all go. You need not hold on to anything at all, including everything that led to your enlightenment. All spiritual practices can only be done in duality; you are past duality and should firmly establish yourself in non-duality now. They were all means to the end and you must let go of them."

*"It's a very lonely last few steps that you must absolutely take **ON YOUR OWN**. There is **NO Guru, Scripture or God** who can or will walk these final steps with you because they can only assist you in duality. In non-duality, you are the only truth in which everything including Guru, God and Scriptures appear. You must walk it alone to the point where there's absolutely NOTHING and the nothing is YOU! You are at the very last and very short transition phase of non-duality, after which you will **NEVER** have a single doubt that **GOD, GURU AND THE SELF** ARE ABSOLUTELY **ONE AND THE SAME IDENTITY**."*

*"The sooner you let go of everything, the sooner you'll be at complete peace and no have conflict whatsoever with **1) Yourself, 2) Others, 3) Life and 4) God.** You will be in eternal bliss and in harmony with absolutely everything in the Universe."*

"This last small transition does feel lonely because there's no guidance whatsoever apart from your own internal Brahman-Self intuitive guidance. Why am I insisting on doing this? It's because the enlightened person can sometimes shy away from accepting that he or she is the Absolute Highest Reality or Truth, that their true Self is non-different from God, because it may sound like blasphemy or egoistic or the mind doesn't want to accept it with reasons like, why can't I perform miracles if I were non-different from God etc."

(Keep in mind, we're talking about your true Brahman-Self being the highest truth and non-different from God, and not your person or mind-body complex.)

"Why am I saying it's a short transition? Because it only takes the time required for you to mentally accept it. Once you've accepted the fact with conviction, it's done! You need not go around telling everyone about it. It will definitely sound like blasphemy to every unenlightened person."

"Simply accept the fact, make the transition and live it experientially. No one else apart from the person who has achieved this same level can even begin to converse with you about it. This final stage is to simply 'accept' and keep it to yourself. The number of people in the world who would be at this stage would not even exceed three figures. And so the enlightened person doesn't go around telling everyone 'I am God' or 'I am the Absolute Truth' to everyone he or she meets. My final word on this is; don't shy away from accepting this Divine truth when the time comes."

"After all these changes and mental acceptance by the mind; when you have absolutely no conflict with what your mind thinks and what you're directly experiencing, when you have no conflict with how others live their lives, when you have no conflict with your life, accepting whatever comes without question, and when you have no conflict with God on what He/She/It should be doing, then you are in total harmony with the Universe. Everything is happening exactly as it should and it's all divine!"

"At this point onwards till the body drops off you are living in the highest state of personhood called the 'turiya' state or 'sahaja samadhi'. Let me explain what this feels like."

"During deep dreamless sleep, when the mind and the body are both at rest, pure consciousness is all that remains but because there is no 'object' to be conscious of, you experience the absence of the Universe, (mentally and physically). This deep sleep state is pure non-dual bliss!"

"There is no sense of time, space or objects. Because the mind has shut down too, there is no reflected consciousness and the person (body-mind complex) has virtually disappeared and only Pure Consciousness your true Brahma-Self exists during that time. The reason I'm telling you all this is because I want you to recall the bliss of deep sleep."

"In the 'turiya' state or 'sahaja samadhi' state that you will be in, you will have that bliss as a constant background in all the activities you do. Can you imagine a state of deep sleep with an awake and alert mind? That's the 'turiya' state and it doesn't come and go, it's a permanent part of your life and will remain till the body drops off."

"You live in that state. You abide as Brahman or Pure Consciousness all the time. It is a state of eternal bliss and peace, which cannot be shaken by any calamites or even the worst tragedies in the world. It's the most 'natural' and 'effortless' state that one can be in. Even thinking a thought will seem like too much effort. It's pure bliss," said Swamiji and he opened the page on where he had made the previous drawing of the landscape.

"David, look at this drawing," said Swamiji holding up the page, *"The Unenlightened person sees this as; Sky at the furthest end, then the mountains, then the trees, then he may say my body and mind sees all that and finally he may say I am conscious of the experience of all this. Reflected-Consciousness is the last thing he may arrive at IF he even gets to think about it."*

"The Underlying reality of the drawing is the Plain sheet of paper that everything appears on. The Unenlightened person never sees the paper; he sees all the different pictures on it that all seem separate from each other. The underlying reality, paper, is never paid attention to, yet it is the reality on which the trees, mountains and sky appear as separate from each other. This is seen using reflected consciousness. Now let me show you what the same picture looks like from the pure consciousness perspective of the enlightened person," said Swamiji and he turned the page and held it backwards facing the fire on the side and letting the light shine through it.

(Ignore the right to left invert)

"David, this is how the fully enlightened person sees the same image. The entire paper is so clear to him that the drawings are only faintly visible. He sees this as one paper on which the sky, mountains and trees are drawn AND none of the drawings appear separate from the paper at any point. In the same way the enlightened Sage sees Pure Consciousness first in which the worldly objects around him appear," explained Swamiji before taking another tea break.

The Unenlightened person clearly sees *MANY drawings on one paper* while the enlightened person clearly sees *ONE paper with many drawings.*

Many Drawings/Reflected Consciousness = Duality.

One Paper/Pure Consciousness = Non-dual.

I'M AWAKE! NOW WHAT?

FULFILLED PROMISES
(3am To Sunrise)

After the break Swamiji carried on with his talk, *"David, let me logically explain how all the promises of enlightenment are fulfilled. I'll use the cinema hall example again. Imagine that there's a movie playing on the screen, your 'person' (body-mind complex) is the main character in the movie and the real you, Brahman, is seated in the hall watching the movie,"* said Swamiji as he took Uchit's notebook and made a drawing of a screen with some nature elements, face masks and a head with a bulb in it. Opposite the screen he drew a sofa on which Mr. Brahman was seated watching the movie on the screen.

Cinema Equivalents:

Movie = Your Life
Screen = The Universe
Character = Person/Reflected Consciousness
Real You = Brahman-Self/Pure Consciousness

"The screen is the world or the Universe where we see everything. Let's name the main character in the movie Mr. Bodymind (The one with a light bulb in his head because he is already enlightened). He represents Reflected Consciousness. Let's name the real Self as Mr. Brahman who is seated as the audience. He represents Pure Consciousness. The enlightened person, Mr. Bodymind, can shift between both reflected and pure consciousness, as you have realized," explained Swamiji as he showed everyone the drawing. *"David, give me some promises of enlightenment,"* asked Swamiji and David quickly responded,

"Some Promises of Enlightenment Include;

You Transcend Pain & Suffering,
All Your Fears Vanish,
You Realize You Are Immortal,
All Your Desires Vanish,
You Live In Eternal Bliss And Peace,
You See The Divinity In Everything,
Freedom From Lust, Anger, Worries, Stress,
Living In Here & Now,
The Universe Is An Illusion/Appearance,
Time & Space Are Illusions,
What Is To Be Known Is Known,
What Is To Be Achieved Is Achieved,
What Is To Be Done Is Done," replied David.

"That's great David! You covered the most important ones. Let's take a look at how this simple example of the cinema hall explains all these promises of enlightenment," said Swamiji.

"Ramlal will you be kind enough to help me out here," asked Swamiji calling out to Ramlal. *"Sure Swamiji,"* came the reply as Ramlal walked over and stood next to Swamiji. *"Ramlal, let's do this in a question and answer format. I'll ask and you answer,"* said Swamiji and Ramlal nodded in agreement.

"Ramlal, **who experiences pain and suffering***?"* asked Swamiji. *"Mr. Bodymind in the movie,"* replied Ramlal. *"Okay, who transcends the pain and suffering?"* asked Swamiji. *"Mr. Bodymind transcends the pain and suffering,"* replied Ramlal swiftly. *"What about Mr. Brahman as the audience?" "Swamiji, he simply witnesses Mr. Bodymind experiencing the pain and suffering,"* replied Ramlal.

"So then, how does Mr. Bodymind transcend the pain and suffering?" asked Swamiji. *"Mr. Bodymind identifies himself as Mr. Brahman. He knows that in reality he is Mr. Brahman and that anything happening to Mr. Bodymind does not affect Mr. Brahman at all. Thus Mr. Bodymind experiences the pain and suffering knowing that he, as Mr. Brahman is untouched by the pain and suffering,"* replied Ramlal.

"*Okay Ramlal.* **Who experiences fear?**" asked Swamiji. "*Mr. Bodymind,*" "*What does he fear?*" "*He fears other people, things and events happening in the movie,*" replied Ramlal. "*Whose fears vanish?*" asked

Swamiji. "*Mr. Bodymind's,*" replied Ramlal. "*How?*" "*Mr. Bodymind identifies himself as Mr. Brahman who knows for a fact that the entire movie is a false reality presented on a screen. Mr. Brahman doesn't fear any person, thing or event displayed on the screen because it's not really happening,*" replied Ramlal confidently.

"**Who is mortal?**" asked Swamiji. "*Mr. Bodymind,*" "*Who realizes he is immortal?*" "*Mr. Bodymind,*" "*Who is immortal?*" "*Mr. Brahman,*" "*How does Mr. Bodymind realize that he is immortal?*" asked Swamiji. "*Mr. Bodymind identifies himself as Mr. Brahman and as far as any movie is concerned, Mr. Brahman was never born and can never die. Only the characters in the movie will die, and not the audience. In the movie, Mr. Bodymind was born and therefore will also die but Mr. Brahman was never born and therefore will never die,*" replied Ramlal with a smile.

Swamiji continued, *"What about the other characters in the movie? Do they have their own Mr. Brahman in the audience to realize?"* asked Swamiji, *"No, there is only one Mr. Brahman that every character can realize as his or her true identity,"* replied Ramlal. *"So what will happen to Mr. Bodymind after he dies?"* *"His body and mind will drop dead and he will remain as the immortal witness, Mr. Brahman,"* replied Ramlal.

"What will happen to a character in the movie that hasn't realized himself as Mr. Brahman?" asked Swamiji. *"He will go through the ups and downs of life and eventually die in the movie, and then move on to another movie, and another movie and another and another until in one movie he realizes himself as Mr. Brahman. When he does that and his character dies in the movie he remains as Mr. Brahman and won't be part of another movie again,"* explained Ramlal much to the amazement of everyone.

Swamiji carried on firing his questions, ***"Who has desires?"*** asked Swamiji. *"Mr. Bodymind,"* replied Ramlal. *"What does he desire?"* *"He desires things, people and events that are in the movie."* *"How do all his desires vanish in an instant?"* asked Swamiji, looking at Ramlal. *"When he identifies himself as Mr. Brahman, he knows that every thing, person or event in the movie is only an illusion on the screen and is not real. All his desires are nullified in one go when he first wakes up to his real identity as Mr. Brahman. Mr. Brahman can enjoy witnessing everything on* *the screen but can never desire anything from the movie, as it's all an illusion,"* replied Ramlal.

*"**Who is not at eternal peace or permanent bliss?**"* asked Swamiji. *"Mr. Bodymind,"* *"Why?"* asked Swamiji.

"Because there's so much going on with his character in the movie that there's hardly any time to rest let alone have peace of mind," replied Ramlal. *"How does he attain permanent bliss and peace?"* asked Swamiji. *"When he identifies himself as Mr. Brahman, he knows that everything in the movie is an illusion. All the stress and havoc-creating events happening in the movie cannot even touch Mr. Brahman. Mr. Brahman witnesses Mr. Bodymind go through all the stress and havoc knowing he is completely untouched by it,"* replied Ramlal.

Swamiji smiled and carried on, *"**Who sees things as good and bad?**"* *"Mr. Bodymind,"* replied Ramlal. *"What and where does he see these?"* asked Swamiji. *"He sees good and evil in his own actions, the actions of the other characters and events that are a part of the movie,"* replied Ramlal.

"Who sees divinity in everyone and everything?" asked Swamiji. *"Mr. Bodymind,"* *"How?"* asked Swamiji. *"Having realized his true identity as Mr. Brahman, he knows that he alone as Mr. Brahman is the true identity of every character on the screen. The characters doing good and evil are only a play of colored light on the screen. There is no real identity of all the characters apart from Mr. Brahman. All the characters on the screen are false identities of the same divinity, Mr. Brahman,"* replied Ramlal

"Who has lust, anger, jealousy, worries and stress?" asked Swamiji. *"Mr. Bodymind"* *"Why does he have them?"* asked Swamiji. *"His desires of different things and interaction with different characters in the movie give rise to different emotions. There are a variety of different emotions that are all genuinely felt by Mr. Bodymind,"* replied Ramlal.

"How does he get freedom from all of them?" asked Swamiji. *"When he realizes his true identity as Mr. Brahman, he knows that every thing, character and event in the movie is an illusion. He realizes that Mr. Brahman is untouched by everything happening on the screen. Mr. Bodymind will not pay attention to any emotion seriously knowing them all to be illusions. They don't disturb Mr. Bodymind. He knows better than to lust after an illusory character or worry about illusory health and wealth, fame and fortune, profit and loss etc. Mr. Bodymind is freed from all such emotions,"* replied Ramlal.

"Who lives in the past and future?" asked Swamiji. *"Mr. Bodymind."* *"How does he do that?"* asked Swamiji. *"He relates to the events that have happened since the beginning of the movie and plans for the future accordingly. He*

has thoughts of the past and the future," replied Ramlal. *"What does that do to him?"* asked Swamiji. *"It keeps him busy so that he doesn't have a chance to realize his true self as Mr. Brahman,"* replied Ramlal. *"How can he realize his true Self as Mr. Brahman?"* asked Swamiji.

"If Mr. Bodymind stopped all his thoughts for even a few seconds, his mind would become still during that time, and he would catch a glimpse of the movie (life) exactly as it appears to Mr. Brahman. If he repeated this for longer and longer periods, he would realize his mind-consciousness slowly expanding to cover the entire screen. He knows that he can't see the entire screen BUT should he turn around to see who is watching the entire screen, he will realize Mr. Brahman is doing it, and if he probes further as to who is Mr. Brahman, he will realize it to be his own true identity and that Mr. Bodymind (himself) is just another illusion on the screen," replied Ramlal and explained further.

"The mind keeps Mr. Bodymind busy with thoughts of the past or the future avoiding the present moment at all costs," said Ramlal. *"What about when Mr. Bodymind realizes his true Self as Mr. Brahman?"* asked Swamiji. *"Then Mr. Bodymind realizes that as Mr. Brahman, there is no past or future on the screen, there is only the present. Mr. Bodymind too abides in the present moment and lets the future unfold on the screen without any thoughts. Mr. Brahman sees only what's on the screen 'here' and 'now',"* replied Ramlal.

*"**Who says the Universe is only an illusion?**"* asked Swamiji. *"Mr. Bodymind."* *"Why?"* asked Swamiji. *"Mr. Bodymind identifies himself as Mr. Brahman and he knows that everything in the movie is just a play of colored light on a screen. He knows that as Mr. Brahman he is watching a movie that has no reality. It's all an illusion or appearance of light projected on a screen,"* replied Ramlal.

*"**Are time and space illusions too?**"* asked Swamiji. *"Yes Swamiji."* *"How?"* asked Swamiji. *"Mr. Bodymind lives through time and space in the movie but having realized himself as Mr. Brahman, he knows that all the space and time projected in the movie is not real. Mr. Brahman sees all the time and space projected in the movie as 'here' and 'now' on the screen. There's no 'there' and 'then' projected on the screen, everything is here and now on the screen, hence the time and space projected appears to be real for unenlightened character in the movie but*

not for Mr. Bodymind who identifies himself as Mr. Brahman," replied Ramlal.

*"**What is to be known is known**, please explain."* asked Swamiji.

"Mr. Bodymind identifies himself as Mr. Brahman and so he knows very well that as Mr. Brahman, everything projected on the screen as the movie is only light. Knowing this everything in the movie is known. The movie is nothing but light. The light can project thousands of images of different things of which some Mr. Bodymind may know or may not know but as Mr. Brahman he knows it's all just light. Knowing light, everything projected in the movie is known," replied Ramlal.

*"**What is to be achieved is achieved**. Please explain"* asked Swamiji. *"From Mr. Bodymind's perspective, after realizing his true Self as Mr. Brahman, he knows that every achievement in the movie by different characters is only an illusion. The highest achievement for a character in the movie would be to realize his true identity as Mr. Brahman. This is actually an achievement because all other achievements in the movie are mere projections of light on a screen,"* replied Ramlal.

*"**What is to be done is done**, please explain,"* asked Swamiji. *"Mr. Bodymind identifying himself as Mr. Brahman knows that whatever he did in the movie as Mr. Bodymind, no matter what path or practices he used to realize his true identity as Mr. Brahman, the highest goal that a character in the movie can achieve is achieved. To achieve that goal, whatever was done was done and nothing more remains to be done. As Mr. Brahman, he just has to witness the life of Mr. Bodymind in the movie until the character dies and he remains in bliss as Mr. Brahman,"* replied Ramlal.

*"**Quickly explain the 'turiya' and 'sahaja samadhi' state using this example**,"* asked Swamiji. *"Swamiji, when Mr. Bodymind starts to identify himself completely as Mr. Brahman, he remains as the witness of the movie for most of the time left until he dies in the movie. Abiding as the witness, he is completely at peace, in bliss and awestruck at how light can project millions of beautiful and creative images (things) in the movie. This constant blissful state of Mr. Brahman experienced by Mr. Bodymind puts him in this completely effortless and permanent blissful 'turiya' or 'sahaja samadhi' state,"* replied Ramlal.

"You surprise me Ramlal, can I test your knowledge further?" asked Swamiji. *"Sure Swamiji,"* replied Ramlal. *"Ramlal, the advanced Vedantin (scholar of Vedanta and non-duality) will point out an error in the image we're using as an example, can you point it out as well?"* asked Swamiji. *"Yes Swamiji, I saw that too but I knew you were explaining it in a simpler way before you got to the advanced stage,"* replied Ramlal, *"Well, what is the error?"* asked Swamiji.

"Swamiji, Mr. Brahman is watching the movie from a distance, that's the error. It denotes duality, the movie and Mr. Brahman. Brahman shouldn't be different from the movie, there should be not even a nanometer of distance between the two, so Mr. Brahman shouldn't be away from the screen," said Ramlal and Swamiji turned the page and drew another drawing. *"I've erased Mr. Brahman and let's assume that the projector too is erased. Now there's only the movie on the screen. Please explain this now?"* asked Swamiji.

I'M AWAKE! NOW WHAT?

ONLY LIGHT & SCREEN

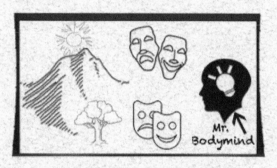

No External Witness or Light Projector.

The Screen Projects Light Upon Itself And The Movie Plays!

I'M AWAKE! NOW WHAT?

"Great, this is correct. The movie is made of light on a screen. There can be no movie without either light or screen; both are essential and non-different from each other. The light represents 'pure consciousness' and the screen represents 'pure existence' and the creative power of the light to project different images represents the Creator or God," said Ramlal.

Light + Screen = Brahman.

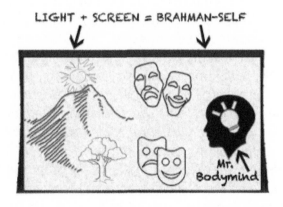

"When Mr. Bodymind is enlightened, he identifies himself as Brahman (light & screen). Brahman is the entire Light on the entire Screen. Mr. Bodymind now knows that as Brahman (light & screen) he is not only the entire movie, but also that the entire movie 'appears' within him. Millions of movies are all nothing but 'light and screen'."

"Light represents pure consciousness, which shines upon the entire screen of pure existence. The screen is self-luminous; it lights up itself (Brahman is known as Self-Luminous, Self-Aware or Self-Conscious). The movie is created by the play of light (play of consciousness), which represents the Creator or God."

"God is the play (of different colors, shapes, images, life forms, worlds, planets, galaxies, multiverses etc.) of consciousness on existence. He is non-different from the entire creation of the movie. He is the whole light-filled screen, and Mr. Bodymind is a part of the lit screen BUT as Brahman, they're both made of the same reality, 'light & screen! The Light, Screen & Movie are non-different from each other just as Consciousness, Existence & Universe are non-different from each other," said Ramlal.

LIGHT + SCREEN = BRAHMAN-SELF

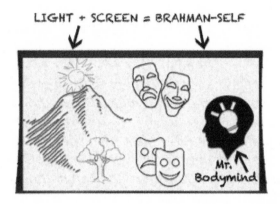

Swamiji asked, *"Is Brahman infinite?"* *"Yes,"* replied Ramlal. *"Is Brahman non-dual?"* *"Yes,"* replied Ramlal. *"Is Brahman doing anything?"* *"No,"* replied Ramlal. *"Is Brahman part of the movie?"* *"No,"* replied Ramlal. *"Is the Movie real?"* *"No,"* replied Ramlal. *"Is the Creator/God (play of light) different from the creation (movie)?"* *"No,"* replied Ramlal.

"Is the character experiencing the ups and downs of life in the movie?" asked Swamiji. *"Yes,"* replied Ramlal. *"Is the Creator/God experiencing the movie?"* *"Yes, (every experience is His),"* replied Ramlal. *"Is Brahman experiencing the movie?"* *"No, everything and everybody in the movie make up the movie that 'appears' on the Absolute Reality of Light & Screen (Brahman),"* replied Ramlal.

"Mr. Bodymind, after identifying himself as Brahman (Light and Screen) can now play out his character in the movie knowing very well that he in fact is the Absolute Reality on which all movies appear," said Ramlal.

"Just for our readers to know, what was this part of the series about," asked Swamiji. ***"Swamiji, this part is about what Mr. Bodymind should expect to experience after having realized himself as Brahman. The few years of life left when Mr. Bodymind knows both Mr. Bodymind and Brahman.*** *It can be tricky or confusing for someone who has no guidance on what to expect. There may be frequent conflicts within the mind, with other characters, with life or with God to those without knowledge or guidance as to what should be expected after realization, till the end of the character's life in the movie,"* replied Ramlal.

"Does this negate the claims of what is to be achieved is achieved and what is to be done is done?" asked Swamiji. *"Not at all! After realization, he has achieved the highest and done what needed to be done. However, without the knowledge or guidance, he will struggle a little to comprehend the new experiences. It's also most likely that 99% of the characters in the movie and the characters around him will not have a clue about his new experiences. Even though I'm not enlightened Swamiji, it's a blessing to know all this,"* replied Ramlal.

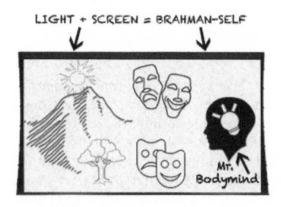

LIGHT + SCREEN = BRAHMAN-SELF

"Swamiji," interrupted Uchit, *"If everything is an illusion, even us sitting here and learning all this is an illusion, are all the teachings of non-duality and Vedanta also an illusion?"* asked Uchit. Swamiji looked at Uchit for a second and then got up to pat him on the back before sitting down again.

"Uchit, I must say, that is the most intelligent question anyone has ever asked me. David, how would you answer that?" asked Swamiji looking at David. *"Swamiji, that is indeed a tricky question, I can't say a clear yes or a clear no,"* replied David.

"Ramlal, let me throw this question at you. The unenlightened character in the movie is asking; Mr. Vedanta you claim that everything in the Universe is an illusion. You too are in and part of the Universe, so tell me now Mr. Vedanta, are you real or are you an illusion too?" asked Swamiji looking amusingly at Ramlal.

"Swamiji, just give me a moment," said Ramlal and he looked at the drawing again, spoke something to himself, scratched his head and thought for about a minute as everyone looked at him eagerly waiting to hear what he would say. Finally Ramlal spoke.

"Swamiji, Vedanta says; In reality I too am an illusion just like you, but do NOT make the GRAVE ERROR of treating me as an illusion BEFORE you have realized what I am talking about. After realizing what I am talking about, you will realize that I too am a part of the illusion!!!" replied Ramlal.

Swamiji quickly got up with a huge smile on his face and gave Ramlal a tight hug patting him on his back. David and Uchit looked on with amazement while clapping their hands for Ramlal.

"Ramlal, that was an exceptional answer and even I could not have put it any better myself," said Swamiji. *"Ramlal, how are you still not enlightened?"* asked David in disbelief, shaking his head.

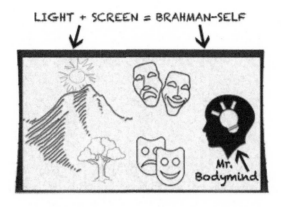

"*Can someone please elaborate?*" asked Uchit looking around at everyone. "*Uchit, I meant to say that just like everything else in the Universe, even the teachings and knowledge of non-duality is an illusion for the enlightened person. This is the truth, BUT the unenlightened person should not make a mistake by considering them to be an illusion UNTIL he or she has not only understood, but REALIZED the teachings,*" said Ramlal looking at Uchit. "*Very well answered, Ramlal,*" said Swamiji patting him on his back.

"*It's all your grace Swamiji, I always listen intently to whatever you say during your talks even though I may be at a distance laying out the table or serving food. You know I love you a lot. Every word you say is like a prayer for me. It's almost sunrise Swamiji, let me serve the tea now before it gets cold,*" said Ramlal and walked to the back of the garden where the table was laid.

Everyone followed him. The tea was still hot in the thermos flasks and they had cookies with freshly buttered toast looking over the mountains, talking and laughing as the sun rose up majestically bringing to life the entire horizon visible from the garden edge.

"David, there's still a final section left to be covered and we'll do that before you leave. Our travel agent will assist you to change and book your return ticket. There's no hurry, but have it booked within a week and I'll see you again for a short final talk," said Swamiji as they dispersed towards their rooms.

SWAMIJI'S FINAL TALK

David, Uchit and Ramlal were up by 11am. After breakfast Uchit drove them to the market place where the travel agent's office was. It was Wednesday and David booked his return flight for the coming Monday. He figured they would leave the ashram on Sunday, spend the night in Muzaffarnagar and then leave for the airport on Monday with plenty of time at hand.

While in the market David picked up some artifacts, handicrafts and other gifts for some of his close friends and family back home. They met Aabha and Panshul as well before leaving back for the ashram. At the ashram they met Swamiji in the library and informed him of their plans.

"That's great!" Exclaimed Swamiji, *"Why don't you go and visit Vivaan and Aarav chachu during the day tomorrow and then spend the night at Chirag chachu's place?"* asked Swamiji, *"You'll be back on Friday, we can have a final talk on Saturday and then you can leave on Sunday,'* suggested Swamiji, *"I'm sure they will all be happy to see you again. It would be a nice gesture from your side too. You should definitely thank them in person before going back,"* said Swamiji.

"Sure Swamiji, that's a great suggestion. We'll leave in the morning," replied David. They all spent the rest of the day doing a few ashram chores and lazing around as they had very few guests during the winter. Next morning Uchit and David were up early and left after breakfast. Uchit drove like he knew the hills in and out. He remembered all the roads they had used the last time they went to meet Vivaan, Aarav and Chirag.

Vivaan chachu was very happy to see David and even more delighted to hear that David had made the breakthrough. As they left Vivaan chachu's clinic, David passed by a fruit vendor and asked him to stock up the fridge outside Vivaan's clinic with different fruits and bottles of water. He paid him and they left. Vivaan chachu was pleasantly surprised at David's kind gesture.

Aarav chachu was over the moon when they met him and he came to know of David's experience. He took both Uchit and David into his prayer room and prayed to God for their well-being and safe journey back home. As they left, David stopped by a flower vendor and paid him to deliver a bunch of fresh flowers daily to Aarav chachu's home for the next three months.

Chirag chachu was happy but not surprised at David's enlightenment experience. *"It was just a matter of when, and not if, it was going to happen,"* he said. They spent the night at Chirag chachu's place and left the next morning back towards the ashram. Passing through the local market, David stopped by a shop that sold mountain climbing equipment and paid for a great pair of expensive climbing boots for Chirag chachu, further on in another shop Uchit selected a set of clothes for Chotu (Chirag chachu's chef and caretaker who had served them pizzas in the Himalayan Mountains).

David paid for all the gifts and had them delivered to Chirag chachu's place. Chotu was overjoyed with the new clothes and Chirag chachu had always wanted those boots for a long time but they were too expensive for a local guy to afford. Back on the road Uchit praised David for his kind gestures that he knew anyone in these remote villages would highly appreciate.

Ramlal was waiting for their return so that they could have lunch together. Uchit finally drove into the ashram parking lot just a few minutes before 2pm. Ramlal had laid the table in the garden and David and Uchit soon joined him. They spoke about their trip as they had their lunch. Uchit's observation was commendable as he described all the enlightened people they had met.

"Sir," said Uchit looking at David, *"Aabha doesn't seem to have changed much externally after enlightenment. He shows no signs of an enlightened being. He works on his passion, which is sculpting. He never felt like he should leave his work and become a guru or spiritual master. In fact he doesn't even talk much about spiritual matters unless one asks him. He's completely engrossed in his art."*

"Panshul on the other hand has found a great way to share his wisdom through a fun fair. He's made creative games that would make one think about the teachings but in a fun way. He is a spiritual master but not the guru type."

"Vivaan chachu Aarav chahcu and Chirag chachu all still do the same things they did before their enlightenment. They still emphasize the purpose and importance of serving, loving, worshipping and meditating. In fact they all take out some time specifically to either serve, worship or meditate."

"Swamiji appears to be very simple but is the most complex one of them all. He has integrated everything that all the other enlightened beings do into his very ordinary daily activities. He is a dedicated spiritual master who is serving and loving everything and everyone as he would God. He simply sees the same divinity within everything and everyone around him and with this inner attitude he covers everything that the other enlightened beings do."

"He smiles at us like he is smiling at God, he teaches us as though a father would teach his son, he only talks about the Absolute Reality all the time and is immersed in it himself. In every talk that we have had the opportunity to be with him, he has taught, served, loved, and worshipped the one divinity within everyone, yet one may feel he is only imparting knowledge. He eats, sleeps, breathes, loves, talks, walks, thinks and everything Brahman. He does nothing, yet he does it all. Simply amazing!" Exclaimed Uchit looking at David and Ramlal.

"Wow Uchit," said Ramlal, *"Even I have never thought of all these enlightened beings in that way before. David, Swamiji said he would see you tomorrow at 9pm so that you're done by midnight and can catch some sleep before you leave on Sunday morning as per your plan. There isn't much to do at the ashram today so you can relax and take some rest,"* said Ramlal as they got up, cleared the table and headed to their rooms.

The next day at precisely 9pm, Swamiji walked into the garden where David and Uchit were seated warming themselves by a fire. *"Did you have a good trip?"* asked Swamiji. *"Yes Swamiji, everyone was happy to see us and I felt good too. Thank you for suggesting us to go and meet them before I leave,"* replied David.

"That's okay," said Swamiji, *"Tonight there's just two topics we need to talk about. The first is how to manage your career and family life after enlightenment and the other is when is it right to start teaching others about the Absolute Reality,"* said Swamiji.

"I'm just going to give you some simple guidelines so that you don't get upset easily when you're back in New York. As far as your career is concerned, you should keep at it and use it to serve as many people as you can. Your life externally will not be very different from what it was when you got here, but internally, yes, there's a huge change. Your workmates and family will notice this change in you. It's a positive change that everyone around you will undoubtedly feel; the only problem you might face is when you try to talk about it. You'll find no one is really interested and may think you've gone mad."

"Try not to reveal what you've experienced to anyone who isn't interested in spirituality. You will more often than not end up in arguments with both parties trying to prove themselves right. Statements such as, I am God, God and I are one, there is no God, I am the Absolute Reality etc. will not be received well by anyone without the knowledge of it."

"Don't try to talk others into doing what you've done or achieving what you've achieved. To put it bluntly, everyone you know will think you have gone nuts or crazy if you share what you now know with them. So take care not to offend others, respect their views and avoid getting into arguments about God, the Universe or the true Self. Most people are not really interested in all this as much as they are about their worldly desires. So try to understand your family's concerns about you, perform your duties as a son, friend, doctor, brother and all other roles that you play. Perform them as you normally would."

"The second topic will make the first one easier to understand. So, should you become a Guru or a spiritual master now that you are awakened? If so, when should you do it? Many enlightened beings become eager to share their knowledge with anyone and everyone they meet. You'll find that most people don't believe them anyway."

*"When you are fully enlightened, there will come a time when you absolutely cannot keep this knowledge to yourself and you are compelled to share it with the world, **then and only then** should you think of guiding others to the Absolute Reality. The wiser you get the less you speak. The wiser you get the more solitude you seek. The Sage never goes out looking for students or disciples and on the other hand he never turns away anyone who comes to him for guidance and wisdom."*

"Everything the Sage speaks is pure gold. His words can be compiled as Holy Scriptures. Every word of the Sage is worth giving your full attention to. His words will never contradict the Absolute Truth."

"Everything the Sage thinks about is for the benefit of humanity He never thinks about himself. His compassion and love for everyone regardless of their background is unconditional. He wants to serve, love and help them transcend pain and suffering just as he himself has done."

"The company of the enlightened master is better then a thousand visits to the temple. His presence alone creates an aura of divine stillness, calmness, love and warmth. He is a walking and talking temple himself and people will not be able to resist coming to him. He attracts people in huge numbers through no effort at all from his side."

"Why am I telling you all this? Because you will undergo the same when people will come to you for guidance, spiritual enlightenment, seeking the truth and God. They will flock to you from places you would never have heard of. They will throw themselves at your feet for your blessings. That is the persona of a true Enlightened Master. Be prepared for when the time comes."

"Your way of communicating the truth may be through art, music, singing, writing, speaking or simply being immersed in the truth and letting others experience it by being around you. There is no set rule that you have to become a teacher sitting on a throne lecturing students, or writing philosophical books on the same. Whenever you feel absolutely compelled to express you will find that the right people who require that knowledge automatically find you or your work."

"They will be the right people who are seeking what you have to offer. Apply the same principle at your work place and around your family and friends. Don't become like the annoying network marketer who only talks about how beneficial his company's products are to everyone. Even though he may be right, everyone avoids him. In the same way, even though you may be talking about the highest reality, your uninterested friends, family and colleagues will find you annoying if they're not interested in it."

"When fully enlightened you will look back and wonder, 'what was the big deal about enlightenment? I was never in bondage and neither is anyone else.' You will be simply abiding in bliss doing 'nothing' and it will seem **so simple** at that time. You may have heard some masters saying that to become enlightened you need not do anything at all, everything you do is a distraction etc."

"Whenever you teach anyone about enlightenment, I want you to keep in mind that everything you did was important to make the breakthrough. After enlightenment it may not seem important but for the unenlightened it is equally important as it was for you before your breakthrough. Every chore you did in the ashram worked towards that breakthrough even though it may seem petty now."

"With this, I end my talk. I have shared all that I had in mind with you. It most certainly will guide you as and when the occasion arises. David it's been an absolute pleasure to share my wisdom with you. Very few people reach this stage. Go back and perform your prescribed duties of life and when the time comes, spread the divine nectar of the Absolute Truth and awaken many more souls to the Absolute Divine Truth within them."

"Yogiji will accompany you to the airport tomorrow. Have a safe flight and I wish you all the best my boy. You have won my heart and I will always be by your side," said Swamiji as he got up and hugged David.

They both had tears in their eyes as they walked towards the table for a last midnight cup of tea with each other. They moon shone brightly and the stars seemed to twinkle a little more than usual. David was too upset to say anything. They all retired to their rooms as Ramlal switched off all the lights one by one in the ashram before going to bed.

I'M AWAKE! NOW WHAT?

DAVID RETURNS TO AMERICA

The next morning after breakfast, Yogiji, David and Uchit got into the car and waved goodbye to an emotional Ramlal as Uchit drove out of the ashram. It was a wonderful day and the sun was shining brightly. By evening they reached Muzaffarnagar and checked into the same hotel for the night. Early next morning, they left for New Delhi. Yogiji handed an envelope from Swamiji with American dollars and a few rupees as payment for his services at the ashram.

David searched his bag and took out the first envelope Swamiji had given him and put all the money into one envelope. He then took out his passport, ticket and wallet from his bag, put in the envelope of money and zipped the bag with all his shopping, gifts and few belongings that he had. *"Uchit, all this is for you. I cannot thank you enough for all that you've done for me. If you ever need anything or there's anything I can do for you, don't hesitate even for a moment to get in touch,"* said David with a shaky quivering voice.

Yogiji looked at the bag, *"David, you're giving away everything you have. At least take the gifts that you bought for your family and friends,"* said Yogiji. *"No Yogiji, I cannot take anything more from this place. What this land has given me can never be re-paid in any way. I am taking the highest possible gift from here. I can't be so cheap as to take material things from here as well. I bow down to this sacred land that has given me something that I could never imagine. I came here looking for God and I found myself,"* said David.

They reached the airport, David checked in and boarded the flight, Uchit was back to his work as a tourist guide in New Delhi and Yogiji took the next train back to Dehradun. (No drama this time.)

David arrived in New York and took a cab back to his apartment. He didn't inform anyone of his return. He had been away for almost a year and a half. Once back in his apartment he called up his parents and the hospital and informed them of his return. Naturally they were overjoyed to hear that he's back. He met up with everyone and told them how wonderful Vatsalya Village and the Himalayan Mountains were, about the hospitality, the food and the generosity of people in the remote villages.

He rejoined work and continued with his passion of surgery. His colleagues noticed that he was always in a good mood and had a constant smile on his face no matter what the situation was in the hospital. People felt calm and relaxed in his presence. The patients in the hospital loved it when he went around to visit them.

He had a genuine care for all of them. His work was going well. The only major external change was that he loved to be alone after work hours. He enjoyed his own company and avoided joining his friends for drinks, parties and weekend getaways. He would stroll into a park and sit simply to observe the world going on around him.

He didn't really feel like going to any places of worship, he never felt the need. Like Swamiji had said, he had stopped praying for anything at all. He enjoyed the bliss of being pure awareness. Everything around him was a 360° movie screen that was playing in ultra high definition and he was witnessing the magic or play of consciousness in awe of the Universe.

He had succeeded in resisting telling anyone about his spiritual achievement in India for almost six months before his parents came to stay with him for a few days in the city. They had retired and lived in the suburbs of California.

He finally did tell his parents about what had happened, which they sort of half believed. It didn't really make sense to them. The words Brahman, Moksha, Pure Consciousness and Pure Existence were unheard of. No one ever thinks about finding out who or what they are in reality. They may spend years finding out other things but who they are in reality was never a question put forward by any parent or school or work place.

David knew they wouldn't really get it and Swamiji had asked him not to tell anyone who wasn't really interested in spirituality. He kept reading spiritual philosophies of different masters in the world and how all the Saints and Sages were talking about the same one underlying reality in different creative ways.

"From the top of the mountain you'll be able to see all the paths that lead to the top," he remembered Swamiji's words. He worked as a surgeon for another two years before deciding that he simply could not keep all this knowledge to himself. he had to tell the world or at least express it out in someway that would benefit mankind.

He quit his job after two years, and with the money he had saved he could afford to buy a lovely little farmhouse outside the city. The monthly rent received from his apartment in the city was enough to cover his monthly expenses on the farm.

He loved being in nature and always remembered his morning meditations at the hilltop near the ashram. At the farm he grew vegetables and kept a few hens and roosters, three cows, six dogs and a small herd of goats and sheep. He earned some extra money by selling the extra vegetables he had grown.

Meanwhile he did keep writing letters to Swamiji, Yogiji and Ramlal in India. Vatsalya Village still didn't have access to Internet facilities or phone network. Letters was still the most convenient way to communicate with them.

He did get in touch with Oliver and Amelia and Otto through email and social media and they were very happy to reconnect with him. David was quite content in life with everything that was going on, it wasn't much, but he chose to give up the busy city life for the quiet farm life.

After another couple of months, David found himself not being able to read or listen to anything more about the Absolute Reality. He couldn't take in any more information. Suddenly one day he felt he should write about his own view of the Absolute Reality. If he were to explain it in his own words out of personal direct experience combined with the knowledge of the scriptures, what would it be like?

With not the least idea on how a book is written, edited or published, he began to scribble notes on separate pieces of paper about what he would write or like to hear about Brahman or Pure Consciousness. He would sit out in the farm and write what came to mind as the sun set in the horizon. Within a couple of months he had written a whole bunch notes that he sorted out and filtered for the final version.

He put the book structure in order and decided to hire an editor and proofreader for assistance to ensure it was done in the proper manner. It took him the next three months to have the complete manuscript ready. He had written the book from the Absolute Reality Point of view. Only about the Absolute Truth and nothing else.

One of his friends father was a publishing agent and he offered to help David get the book published. They sent out the manuscript to many top publishing houses and waited for a response which usually took anywhere between 2-4 months. Finally after a wait of three months, the biggest publishing house in the country offered to publish and release the book within the next couple of months.

One fine day as David sipped his morning coffee out on his farm, the postman walked in with a letter from the ashram. Swamiji's health wasn't too good and the doctors had done their best but to no avail. Swamiji wanted to see David again and so Ramlal had written the letter requesting David to come over and spend some time with Swamiji if he could.

Within a week, David was on a flight to New Delhi. He had arranged for someone to look after his farm and feed the animals on time until his return. Uchit received David at the airport and they drove to the Himalayan Village reaching the next day. Swamiji's health wasn't too good. He had been diagnosed with pancreatic cancer at the last stage and the doctors had given him six months at most to live.

David was heartbroken to hear this and he decided he would stay by Swamiji's side till the end. Swamiji could still walk about in the ashram for about a month after David arrived. He was in a lot of physical pain and after a month, he was shifted to a hospital in Dehradun.

David did his best as everyone else did to look after Swamiji. Even though he was in pain, Swamiji often smiled and spoke with love to everyone who visited him.

"David, I'll be gone by next week. I know it and it's not a problem. I don't want any of you to feel sad or depressed, rather I would like you to get back to your work and life as soon as possible. David, it's time to perform your divine work of enlightening other people. You will travel the world over and sprinkle the nectar of the Supreme Being that will awaken many people."

"You need not build an ashram in your country but you will carry on with the work that my master bestowed upon me and that I am now bestowing upon you. My body and mind have served me well and at the end they have to drop off, that's life but the end of life doesn't mean the end of me. I will always be with you. And besides, where can I go? I'm here right now and after the death of the body, I will still be here as I am right now. I'd like to request that no one except David visit me for the next few days please," said Swamiji looking at Uchit, Yogiji, Ramlal and David. His face was glowing and his eyes were sparkling as he spoke all this. Everyone's eyes were filled with tears

For the next few days, only David went to the hospital and stayed with Swamiji all day. He helped Swamiji sit up, they watched some comedy shows on TV to lighten the mood and David did all he could to keep Swamiji entertained and happy.

"David, do you still meditate?" asked Swamiji. *"Yes Swamiji, I still do it in the morning before I start my day,"* replied David. *"That's great, come in early tomorrow morning and let's sit for meditation together,"* said Swamiji. *"That would be awesome Swamiji,"* replied David excitedly because no one had ever seen Swamiji sit in meditation.

David was at the hospital at 5am the next morning. He helped Swamiji sit up on the bed and made him comfortable. David sat opposite him on a chair and as they closed their eyes, suddenly David felt like the whole world had become still in an instant. Silence suddenly prevailed everything. David could hear nothing at all. They sat and David focused and concentrated at the eye center. He had never experienced such stillness and silence even at the hilltop.

They were both in deep meditation and about an hour later, David was startled out of meditation by a loud noise. He quickly opened his eyes and realized the picture of Swamiji's Master that was kept beside his bed had fallen and the glass had shattered to pieces. David got up to pick the picture and as he looked at Swamiji still seated, he noticed Swamiji wasn't breathing, he touched Swamiji and his body was cold all over. Immediately David pressed the alarm button as he tried to revive a heartbeat in Swamiji's body. The nurses rushed in and the doctor on duty came rushing in. They tried everything to revive Swamiji, but he was gone.

David was heartbroken as he watched the doctors and nurses, cover Swamiji's body and prepare all the necessary paperwork. In India, the dead body is cremated the same day and arrangements were made for Swamiji's body to be taken to Vatsalya Village Crematorium where the funeral took place the same evening.

Everyone was sad at the ashram as people poured in from all parts of the country during the next few weeks to offer their condolences. David, Uchit, Ramlal and Yogiji looked after everyone who came. David stayed on for another few weeks as they converted the ashram into a shrine for everyone who knew Swamiji to come and seek his blessings.

Swamiji's room was kept intact as he had kept it, the bed sheets and pillowcases were changed everyday and Ramlal kept flowers on the bed daily in the morning. Visitors were allowed to go in and spend time sitting in the room.

After almost four months when everything was almost back to normal at the ashram, David returned to America. When he landed and switched on his mobile phone, immediately there was a flood of messages and emails and as he went through them on the way home, most of them were from his friend's father and the publishing company. He was to get back to them as soon as possible.

David immediately called his friend's father who narrated over the phone what had happened. During the time David was in India, his book was released and had become a New York bestseller within a month. The publishing house had lined up events for David around the country but no one could get in touch with him. David hadn't informed anyone before leaving for India.

The book had sold over half a million copies around the world in just over two months. David had become the most sought after spiritual master yet he couldn't be located. His book was a raging success and praised all over by major spiritual masters around the world.

He got in touch with the people at the publishing house who were relieved to hear from him. Immediately a tour around the country was organized and David found himself in front of crowds who wanted to hear from him. They wanted to know his story and sought guidance about realizing the truth. At his first ever talk, he was asked by someone, *"Could you please tell us your Master's highest teaching in one sentence?"* David's reply stunned everyone in the hall.

"I Am My Master's Highest Teaching!"
Exclaimed David.

Everywhere he held his talks, people were bathed in his love and mesmerized by his charisma. He set up a condition for all his events; no one will be charged any money to attend his talks and he would not charge a penny for the talks either. He convinced the publishing house to cover their expenses through other means such as sponsorship, donations and sale of books and merchandise at the events.

He remembered Swamiji's words in the hospital, *"David, it's time to perform your divine work of enlightening other people. You will travel the world over and sprinkle the nectar of the Supreme Being that will awaken many people. You need not build an ashram in your country but you will carry on with the work that my master bestowed upon me and that I am now bestowing upon you."*

David picked up a copy of his book and smiled as he opened the first page. He had dedicated the book to Swamiji. He flipped through a few pages and as he closed the book he couldn't remember why he chose such a title. It seemed wrong and correct at the same time.

"I Am Conscious Ness"
https://www.amazon.com/dp/B07S724Z36

I'M AWAKE! NOW WHAT?

EXTRA NOTES

This is the end of part 5 of the "I Am Consciousness" Series. Most of the scriptures end at enlightenment and very few books have been written about what to expect 'after enlightenment'. If you have the knowledge it will be a very smooth and pleasant transition to becoming fully enlightened, however, if you attained enlightenment and don't know what to expect, it can be a struggle between the mind and direct experience until you analyze and accept the changes. Of course it's advisable to know what to expect and accept it graciously knowing it's a part of the process.

Full enlightenment ends at *nothing,* with the *nothing* being your true identity. One has to discard everything including the scriptures, knowledge, gurus, spiritual masters and even God to get to this full enlightenment stage. At this point there is nothing but the Self as Pure Bliss! The Self is the only Truth and everything is an illusion, including all spiritual practices and the knowledge of non-duality!

The changes discussed may seem unbelievable to the unenlightened person. Everything mentioned in this part can only be directly experienced to believe it. Shifting from reflected consciousness to pure consciousness is something only the spiritually awake person can do at will. It is the difference between identifying oneself as the ego and as pure consciousness or awareness.

The enlightened person appears completely normal and lives a normal life that may be seen externally, but internally, he lives as pure bliss knowing this the Universe to be an appearance within his own true immortal Self.

Even if you have not yet made the breakthrough as yet, let me tell how fortunate you are. Out of the 7-8 billion people there are on this planet, only a handful are pulled towards realizing the truth. The Upanishads state that it is only after millions of years that are we blessed with the human life form. It is only the human being that is capable of realizing the truth because only human minds possess an intellect that is the key to Self-realization.

Therefore we shouldn't waste this life chasing after temporary pleasures of the world but should instead work towards realizing our true immortal Self. Question: What happens if we don't realize our true Self?

The Katha Upanishad says, *"Part 2, Chapter 3, Verse 4; If anyone is able to attain the knowledge of Brahman before death, he gets liberation in this very life; otherwise he is born again and again in this world and other worlds."* It may be another few million lives before we are blessed with the human form again.

And what happens to all the effort we put into seeking the truth if we still fail to realize it in this lifetime? It is said that no effort put towards Self-realization is wasted and whenever we are re-born in the human form again, we will automatically pick up from where we stopped. (This is mentioned in the Bhagavad Gita Chapter 6, Verse 41-43)

Unfortunately we lost Swamiji in this part of the series. David had his first book published about the Absolute Reality in his own words that became a bestseller. The book is titled "I Am Conscious Ness" which is the last part of this book series as well.

Join us in the **last part** and read about the Absolute Truth as it written from a Western point of view with knowledge from the East. David's creativity in describing the Absolute is remarkable as he covers every aspect of the Individual, the Universe and the Absolute!

"Not The Highest Teachings
BUT
Teachings Of The Highest!"
–David Smith

"I Am Conscious Ness"
https://www.amazon.com/dp/B07S724Z36

ABOUT THE AUTHOR

Sukhdev Virdee was born and brought up in Nairobi, Kenya. Since childhood he was very inclined towards spirituality and music. After his studies he chose to take up music as a profession. He learnt how to play the keyboards and started performing live on stage at the age of nineteen. He later went to London and completed a BTEC in Music Production and Performance.

He later flew to Mumbai, India to pursue his dream of singing and composing music in the largest Indian Entertainment Industry. His debut pop-album became a chartbuster making him a popular household name in India and across the world. Mumbai became his home where he is known for his high energy live performances and this popularity took him to several countries across every continent on the planet to perform live for huge audiences.

A few more albums and singles followed after that. He was living the life that every young person looks up to even today. He had created a name for himself and enjoyed the name, fame and fortune that most singers dream of but never get to live. During all this he was totally oblivious of what life had in store for him in the coming years.

Just before his 40th birthday, when he was going through a rather rough patch in life, three of his friends gifted him the Bhagavad Gita out of the blue. These were friends that he met only occasionally and yet within two weeks three different people gifted him the Bhagavad Gita that would change his life completely. He read the Bhagavad Gita and felt Lord Krishna was speaking directly to him. It completely changed his outlook towards life as he followed the teachings in the Bhagavad Gita as best as he could.

Just over a year later, one fine morning after he woke up from his morning meditation and walked towards his temple in the house, his body completely froze and in an instant he had become one with the entire Universe. Time stood still and every particle of the entire Universe was alive and shining in bright golden light and he was the light. He was no longer limited to just his body or mind, he was everywhere at the same time and everything was one with him.

This Spiritual awakening experience turned his life upside down and inside out. All desires for anything worldly vanished, fear of death vanished, love and compassion for entire humanity and nature arose and he could feel and experience the Supreme Being in everything.

Not knowing exactly what had happened and what to do next, he sought out several resources before he was pointed towards the Upanishads that answered all his questions as to what had happened, what led to it and what to do after such an awakening.

After years of studying the Vedanta texts he is now an expert on non-dual Vedanta through not only intellectual and philosophical knowledge but most importantly with his own personal direct experience everyday.

He has put all his heart and soul into writing the *"I Am Consciousness"* book series that include the highest knowledge of the Upanishads and his own direct experience and knowledge of the Supreme Being.

The series has been written with the absolute conviction that you, the reader, can realize your true immortal Universal Self too, that you are pure bliss and completely unaffected by all pain and suffering.

The promise of all spirituality is that one transcends pain and sorrow in this world, not that pain and sorrow don't come, but that the realized being is untouched by it. One realizes that their true nature is immortal, that they are one with the Universe. Would a being that realizes that he or she is one with the Universe ever want to accumulate anything in this world?

No, the True Saint or Sage who is Self-Realized makes do with only the very basic necessities required to live an honest decent life. They don't look to gain wealth, become famous, build an empire or any such sort of selfish activities.

Their main focus becomes serving humanity selflessly and uplifting others to help them realize their true nature so that they too can transcend suffering and realize their Oneness with the Universe. Sukhdev aims to do just that through his music, art and writing in the remaining days that he has left in this mortal body.

"I Am Consciousness"
6 Book Series
A Journey From Seeker
To Enlightened Master
Available As
E-books & Paperbacks
On Amazon & Other Digital Stores

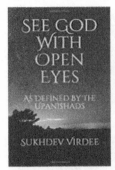 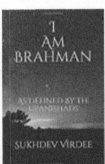 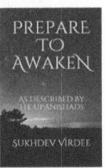

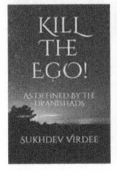 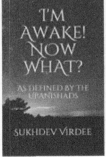 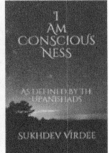

Available As
E-books & Paperbacks
On Amazon & Other Digital Stores

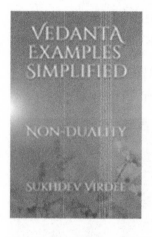

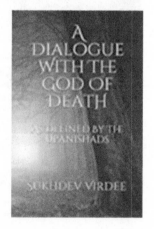

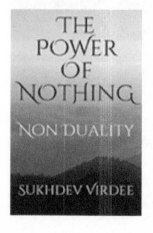

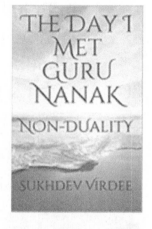

Made in the USA
Las Vegas, NV
17 October 2022

57515867R00090